DATE DUE

MAN-MADE LAKES

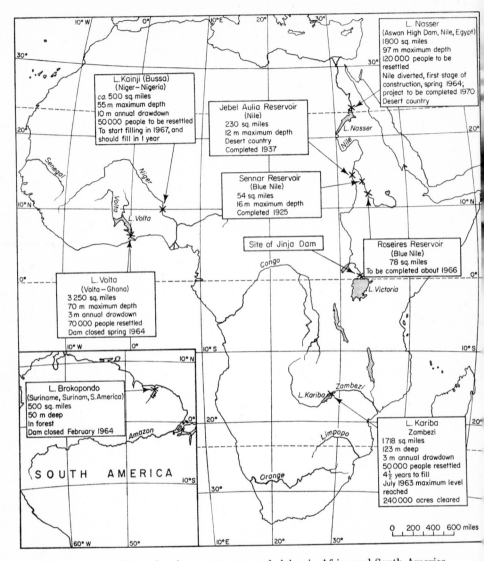

FRONTISPIECE. Sites of major recent man-made lakes in Africa and South America.

In addition to the lakes shown on this map, numerous smaller man-made lakes and dams scatter the drier parts of the two continents. Lake Victoria, a natural lake over 26 000 sq. miles in area, is now controlled by the Owen Falls Dam built across the out-flowing Nile at Jinja (completed 1964) for hydro-electric purposes. Lakes Kariba, Volta and Kainji lie in bush which has presented clearance problems; Lake Nasser is in desert, and Lake Brokopondo in high forest where no clearing was attempted. Extensive invasions of floating water plants have occurred in some of the Nile lakes, Lake Kariba and Lake Brokopondo. Game animals stranded by rising water were rescued under "Operation Noah" at Kariba and a similar scheme at Brokopondo. Valuable fisheries have already been developed on Kariba and some of the other lakes.

SYMPOSIA OF THE INSTITUTE OF BIOLOGY No. 15

MAN-MADE LAKES

(Proceedings of a Symposium held at
the Royal Geographical Society, London
on 30 September and 1 October 1965)

Edited by

R. H. LOWE-McCONNELL

1966

Published for the
INSTITUTE OF BIOLOGY
by
ACADEMIC PRESS
LONDON and NEW YORK

ACADEMIC PRESS INC. (LONDON) LTD
Berkeley Square House
Berkeley Square
London, W.1

U.S. Edition published by
ACADEMIC PRESS INC.
111 Fifth Avenue
New York, New York 10003

Library of Congress Catalog Card Number: 65-27735

PRINTED IN GREAT BRITAIN BY
W. S. COWELL LTD.
AT THE BUTTER MARKET, IPSWICH

Contributors

LEONARD H. BROWN, *Mid-Northamptonshire Water Board, Cliftonville, Northampton, England*

O. DAVIES, *Volta Basin Research Project, University of Ghana, Accra, Ghana*

D. W. EWER, *Volta Basin Research Project, University of Ghana, Accra, Ghana*

H. C. GILSON, *Freshwater Biological Association, Ambleside, Westmorland, England*

D. HARDING, *Fisheries Research Station, Game Fisheries Department, Chilanga, Zambia*

G. U. HOUGHTON, *South Essex Waterworks Co., Colchester, England*

JACKSON, P. B. N., *Food and Agricultural Organization of the United Nations, UNSF Fisheries Research Project, Lake Victoria, Jinja, Uganda*

W. E. KERSHAW, *Liverpool School of Tropical Medicine, Liverpool, England*

FRANK LAW, *Fylde Water Board, Blackpool, England*

P. LEENTVAAR, *State Institute for Nature Conservation Research (RIVON), Zeist, The Netherlands*

D. J. LEWIS, *c/o British Museum (Natural History), London, England*

E. C. S. LITTLE, *Weed Research Organization, Begbroke Hill, Oxford, England*

K. A. PYEFINCH, *Freshwater Fisheries Laboratory, Pitlochry, Scotland*

JULIAN RZOSKA, *Freshwater Productivity Section, International Biological Programme, and Sir John Cass College, London, England*

T. SCUDDER, *California Institute of Technology, Pasadena, California, U.S.A.*

RICHARD H. STROUD, *Sport Fishery Research Foundation and Sport Fishing Institute, Washington, D.C., U.S.A.*

K. F. VAAS, *Hydrobiological Institute, Yerseke, The Netherlands*

B. B. WADDY, *London School of Hygiene and Tropical Medicine, London, England*

E. B. WORTHINGTON, *International Biological Programme, London, England*

Participants in the Discussions

G. L. ATKINSON-WILLES, *Wildfowl Trust, Slimbridge, Gloucestershire, England*

R. S. A. BEAUCHAMP, *Central Electricity Research Laboratories, Leatherhead, Surrey, England*

W. C. BECKMAN, *Food and Agriculture Organization, Rome, Italy*

C. G. L. BERTRAM, *St. John's College, University of Cambridge, Cambridge, England*

A. F. DE BONT, *Box 118, Leopoldville, Congo, Africa*

A. K. BISWAS, *Department of Civil Engineering, University of Strathclyde, Glasgow, Scotland*

J. G. CORLETT, *M.A.F.F. Fisheries Laboratory, Lowestoft, England*

D. CRAGG-HINE, *A. & B. Laboratory, Drakelow Power Station, Drakelow, Burton-on-Trent, England*

BARBARA DOUGLAS, *Department of Botany, University of Leeds, England*

R. L. DREW, *Department of Civil Engineering, University of Strathclyde, Glasgow, Scotland*

H. FISH, *Essex River Authority, Chelmsford, Essex, England*

S. E. H. FORD, *Binnie & Partners, London, England*

A. V. GIFKINS, *Salmon & Trout Association, London, England*

J. D. GWYNN, *Balbour Beatty & Co. Ltd., London, England*

I. P. HAIGH, *Alexander Gibbs & Partners, London, England*

J. D. HAMILTON, *Paisley College of Technology, Paisley, Renfrewshire, Scotland*

C. F. HICKLING, *95 Greenway, London, England*

M. J. HOLDEN, *M.A.F.F., Fisheries Laboratory, Lowestoft, England*

T. HUXLEY, *Nature Conservancy, Edinburgh, Scotland*

SIR ROBERT JACKSON, *United Nations Special Fund, New York, U.S.A.*

L. B. JOERIS, *Lake Kariba Fisheries Research Institute, Chilanga (Lusaka), Zambia*

R. H. LOWE-McCONNELL, *Streatwick, Streat, Hassocks, Sussex, England*

O. E. LOWENSTEIN, *Department of Zoology, University of Birmingham, England*

J. W. G. LUND, *Freshwater Biological Association, Ambleside, Westmorland, England*

N. C. MORGAN, *Nature Conservancy, Edinburgh, Scotland*

LILY NEWTON, *Department of Botany, University College, Aberystwyth, Wales*

G. C. S. Oliver, *Corby (Northants) and District Water Co., Corby, Northamptonshire, England*

F. T. K. Pentelow, *26 Old Slade Lane, Iver, Buckinghamshire, England*

B. Rydz, *Water Resources Board, Reading, Berkshire, England*

A. Sandison, *British Museum, London, England*

I. R. Smith, *Nature Conservancy, Edinburgh, Scotland*

B. Steele, *Weed Research Organization, Begbroke Hill, Oxford, England*

J. Talling, *Freshwater Biological Association, Ambleside, Westmorland, England*

E. White, *Department of Zoology, University of Liverpool, England*

F. White, *Kirkfield Farm, Walpole St. Peter, Norfolk, England*

C. M. Yonge, *Zoology Department, University of Glasgow, Scotland*

Preface

Man-made lakes are becoming increasingly important in many parts of the world. In Africa alone the lakes behind the dams just completed or under construction, on the Zambezi at Kariba, the Volta, the Niger at Kainji, and the Nile at Aswan, are inundating over 7 000 sq. miles of country, and some 200 000 people are having to be resettled from these flooded areas. In addition to hydro-electric power, for which these dams were primarily constructed, their creation provides many new opportunities, for irrigated farming, for fisheries development to supply much-needed protein, for transport, and for national parks and tourism. The resettlement of the people also provides openings for inducing social and economic change and for improving health. But to achieve all these things, each new lake must be considered as part of an integrated lake basin development programme, and multidisciplinary research is essential. Soil and agricultural surveys have to be made to find suitable land for those displaced, and biologists have to study the many problems of flooding, bush-clearing, aquatic weed control, and development and teaching of new fishing methods.

In the United Kingdom, where demand for water continues to rise at 4–5% per annum, man-made lakes also present many problems, and the old idea of a reservoir for water supply only is giving way, under pressure, to the new idea of multipurpose use, including recreation. Reclamation of estuaries for freshwater supply as well as for agricultural land has long been carried out in Holland, and the feasibility of doing something similar in this country is now being considered in relation to Morecambe Bay, the Solway Firth, and possibly the Wash. In Hong Kong an arm of the sea is to become a freshwater reservoir very soon.

The integrated study of man-made lakes is comparatively new, and information is widely scattered. Each new lake is helped by experience derived from its predecessors, which adds to the importance of collating data as soon as they are available. This present Symposium was attended by over two hundred delegates, including biologists, hydrologists, engineers, sociologists, and those interested in the medical and other aspects of new lakes. As the papers had been circulated before the meeting, the contributors spoke briefly, allowing the maximum time for discussion.

This symposium was particularly valuable for two reasons. Firstly it brought together engineers and scientists of many disciplines all

A*   ix

concerned with some aspect of the development of new lakes. Secondly, it also brought together, in many cases for the first time, people working on similar problems in widely separated parts of the world, especially the tropics, who will continue to keep in touch with one another. Thanks are due to the Royal Society, the Ford Foundation, the Food and Agriculture Organization of the United Nations, and the American Conservation Association, who provided funds to enable some of the far-flung delegates to attend the meeting.

The need for studies on man-made lakes has recently been recognized in the U.S.S.R. where a new institute has been formed for this purpose. In the U.S.A. the Africa Science Board of the National Academy of Sciences, Washington, D.C., has just produced a selected guide to the literature on man-made lakes, copies of which were available at the Symposium. In addition, a bibliography on reservoir fishery biology in North America has just been issued by the Department of the Interior, Fish and Wildlife Service Washington, D.C.

Those working on tropical problems emphasized the need for another meeting to bring the working scientists and engineers together again in a few years' time—preferably on one of the great new lakes in the tropics.

February 1966   R. H. LOWE-McCONNELL

Contents

The Natural History of Man-made Lakes
in the Tropics

Introductory Survey

E. B. WORTHINGTON

International Biological Programme, London, England

Large stretches of open water have great influence on all forms of plant, animal and human life, especially when situated within a continental region. From the human point of view the main effects are on climate, water supply, fisheries, forests, agriculture, transport, health and the natural beauty of the countryside. Because large lakes create countless opportunities nearly all their influences are to human advantage, and a glance at a map of population distribution shows how people tend to cluster around them. Lake Victoria is a good example, or the northern end of Lake Nyasa (now Lake Malawi).

The new artificial lakes, whether made primarily for hydro-electric power as at Kariba, Volta, Kainji and Brokopondo, or for water conservation, as at Nasser, Jebel Auliya and Roseires, will in all probability have influences on the local people and their habitat similar to those of natural lakes. To provide a few of the background facts about them, some data are set out in Table I.

TABLE I

Lake	Area at high stage (km²)	Altitude (m)	Maximum depth (m)	Maximum drawdown (m)	Ratio of annual outflow to volume	No. of people moved
Man-made lakes						
Lake Kariba	4 300	530	125	3	1:9	50 000
Lake Volta	8 500	92	70	3	1:4	70 000
Kainji Lake	1 280	155	55	10	4:1	50 000
Lake Nasser	5 000	185	97		1:2	120 000
Jebel Auliya reservoir	600	377	12	ca 6	8:1	—
Sennar reservoir	140	422	16	ca 17	70:1	—
Roseires reservoir	200	480		ca 42	16:1	—
Lake Brokopondo (S. America)	1 500	ca 25	50			—
Natural lakes						
Lake Albert	5 283	672	48			—
Lake Tanganyika	39 000	844	1 500		ca 1:∞	—
Lake Victoria	67 679	1 234	90			—

The very idea of a large lake in the rather dry savanna lands of west or central Africa is so strange that it takes time for people to appreciate the implications. The experience from those countries lucky enough to contain large natural lakes should therefore be of great advantage in the planning stages of artificial lakes; and a good deal of foresight is desirable to assess the changes which will occur, to prepare for them, to take advantage of those that are favourable, and to take measures against those that are not. This involves research of a multi-disciplinary kind, working up the food chain from the inorganic and physical factors, through the plant links and the animal links to man himself.

Such research, which is desirable before, during and after inundation, should by no means be limited to the water, although in this there are very obvious changes of human importance, particularly in fisheries and the vectors of disease. The research should extend to a substantial zone of land around the lake, which will come under its influence. This zone like the lake itself needs advance planning, perhaps for settlement schemes to provide new opportunities for the people whose land is drowned, perhaps for wild nature. One purpose may be to attract tourists and visitors to see a National Park or to go angling.

Let us take a quick look at the main factors of the environment, and the natural resources, including mankind, in order to see what kind of changes are likely following a major inundation in the tropics.

Firstly we have the rocks, the surface of the land and the atmosphere above it: geology, physiography and climatology. Inundation may have a substantial effect on the water table in an area surrounding the new lake basin, and perhaps in recharging subterranean aquifers and thereby giving better opportunity for water supply over a wide area. The effects on the amelioration of climate are less easy to forecast; but it is well to remember that Lake Victoria and some other natural lakes create their own climatic system with daily sea breezes and nightly land breezes, with consequent influence on rainfall, vegetation and agricultural opportunity. Clearly there is a strong case for hydrogeological and climatological study to measure any changes which follow inundation.

The water itself, whose quantity and quality depends on the physical factors together with the influence of vegetation, is the most obvious subject for study. From a quantitative point of view this is looked after pretty well by the engineer hydrologists; but the qualitative changes may be even more important from the biological or human standpoint. Among major changes to study are the de-oxygenation of water, consequent on the rotting of drowned vegetation. This has been most prominent perhaps at Brokopondo and Volta, but has been a major factor also at Kariba and many smaller impoundments. Another changing factor is the organic content of the water which in the early years of inundation appears to favour a big development of floating water plants. The water circulation and distribution of nutrients is basic to all biological studies for it will control the development of plankton, benthos, fish and fisheries, snails and mosquitoes.

In plant sciences it is not only the phytoplankton and floating vegetation which demand study, but on land the influence of water table and climatic amelioration on vegetation and the opportunities for agriculture and forestry which follow therefrom. We should not forget cultivation on the exposed bottom deposits when the lake is at low stage, and irrigated agriculture along the margins by pump.

On the animal side the development of fish and fisheries is one of the major results of inundation, and here it is well to remember that the raw materials for creating a fishery are profoundly different in different places, even within Africa. In that continent there are at least six distinctive hydrobiological regions based on the indigenous fish.

Profound changes will take place also in the bird and mammalian fauna, both terrestrial and aquatic, and this, coupled with the natural vegetation, suggests the opportunities for wildlife conservation in the form of National Parks along the lake shore, tied in with the tourist industry. There is no doubt that every large man-made lake provides an opportunity for this and to miss it, for example by allowing indiscriminate settlement all around the lake, could be a crime against posterity.

Turning to the human communities there are obvious opportunities around man-made lakes for all stages in the succession of man's activities, for the hunter, the fisherman, the pastoralist, the cultivator and the urban and industrial worker. Before the inundation, the opportunities for human activity are, as a rule, very much more limited. Thus the creation of a lake is generally followed by a diversification and a flowering of human endeavour. Scudder will tell us of his experience with the Valley Tonga at Kariba, the Nubians above Aswan and what happened subsequent to the disruption of their former life (pp. 99–108).

We shall hear at first hand about Kariba from Harding (pp. 7–19), where there is already a good deal of experience following the inundation, about Volta from Ewer (pp. 21–30), and Brokopondo from Leentvaar (pp. 33–41). At all three there is a good deal of research in progress on the aquatic side. The lake impounded at Kainji on the River Niger, where inundation does not start for a year or so, provides particularly good opportunities for study before, during and after flooding. White, who has organized biological investigations there, will tell us something about them (p. 47). I am sorry that the artificial lakes of the Nile system, with their rather complex but different problems, do not figure specially in the programme. It is well to remember that Lake Victoria, at the head of the White Nile system, is already the largest reservoir in the world, since its level and its discharge are fully controlled by the Owen Falls Dam. Above Khartoum on the White Nile, the Jebel Auliya reservoir, though not one of the largest in Africa, is one of the most interesting and has been studied from hydrobiological, fisheries and health viewpoints. Lately it has been a centre for the study and control of *Eichhornia*. Rzoska will tell us something of its hydrobiology (p. 47) and Lewis (p. 43–45) about its medical entomology. Some attention has also been given to the reservoir on the Blue Nile impounded at Sennar. There is now a major opportunity at the new Blue Nile reservoir impounded at Roseires, an opportunity which I fear may be missed, except for the influence of the engineering works on the management of the important Dinda National Park nearby.

Further downstream the greatest of all dams, above Aswan, provides one of the biggest opportunities and the greatest urgency for the kind of inter-disciplinary research in which we are interested. Here Lake Nasser, now filling, is very different from the other man-made lakes of Africa, for there is almost no vegetation to be inundated. There are, however, great problems of hydrology and of hydrogeology as well as of hydrobiology. Already a hydrobiological institute has been built there. Considerable study has been devoted to the desert water tables, and to the possibilities of seepage from Lake Nasser, perhaps even into the New Valley to the west. There are substantial plans maturing for a full scale Lake Research Institute of a multi-disciplinary kind. A particular problem of the interim here is the effect on hydrobiology and fisheries of a molecular film of acetyl alcohol, which the hydrological engineers have suggested should be applied to the lake to reduce evaporation. The Special Fund of U.N. has been much interested in research on Lake Nasser.

Finally I would draw attention to the International Biological Programme and the International Hydrological Decade, both now in their first year, and due to run contemporaneously for a period which is likely to cover the most interesting changes in the great man-made lakes of tropical Africa. The tremendous increase in biological productivity following an inundation and its return to a new steady level after a period of years is fairly well known for temperate reservoirs, but little yet for the tropics. The influence of impoundments on the flow of rivers, and on various aspects of the hydrological cycle, including evaporation, transpiration, seepage, run off and water quality, is an important feature of the hydrological decade. Clearly the two need to get into very close co-ordination in planning and carrying out research programmes, and this symposium may help them to do so.

Lake Kariba
The Hydrology and Development of Fisheries

D. HARDING

*Fisheries Research Station, Game Fisheries Department, Chilanga, Zambia**

INTRODUCTION

Lake Kariba was formed when the great dam across the Zambezi was completed in December 1958. The lake flooded the entire middle section of the Zambezi valley and took four and a half years to fill, by which time it was about 175 miles long and 50 miles wide, with a surface area of 1 100 000 acres, an average depth of 150 ft and a maximum depth of 375 ft near the dam wall.

The main purpose of Kariba was to produce hydro-electric power for the industries of Rhodesia and Zambia. The power station, sited on the south bank has been operating near its full capacity since 1963, and in its final phase will be capable of producing more than 800 MW. It had, however, been realized that an important fishing industry could be developed on the lake, indeed the fishing potential was recognized even before the construction of the dam. General studies on the limnology and fisheries in the Zambezi River began in 1956 and these researches continued in the newly forming lake.

The uniqueness of Kariba is not merely that it is one of the largest manmade lakes in the world, that its creation necessitated the resettlement of hundreds of the Tonga tribe and resulted in the much publicized Operation Noah, but that, from a hydrobiological standpoint, it is of unrivalled interest. The investigations in this field and facts concerning the development of the fisheries are described in this paper.

METHODS

Briefly the investigations were concerned with the physico-chemical environment, the ecology and biology of fish in the changed environment, and the build-up of the commercial fisheries.

Physico-chemical studies were carried out mainly at two stations near the dam wall where temperatures, dissolved oxygen and general chemical

*Present address: M.A.F.F., Fisheries Laboratory, Lowestoft, England.

analyses were estimated at regular intervals and compared with data collected from other parts of the lake.

Research on the ecology and biology of fish began by making sampling surveys of various areas of the lake and from standard fishing stations using fleets of graded gill nets. The gill net fleets used were either five nets of 2–6 in. stretched mesh in 1 in. mesh increments or ten nets of 1–6 in. stretched mesh in $\frac{1}{2}$-in. mesh increments. Towards the end of the survey it was necessary to use nets ranging up to 8 in. stretched mesh in the fleets to cover the full size range of the various species of fish.

The commercial fishery which developed in the lake was sampled by recording total daily landings at eight or nine of the major fishing villages which sprang up on the lake shore. At each station the recorders counted the numbers of each species and a total weight landed by individual fishermen. In later studies when the staff became more proficient, lengths of the different species were also measured. These records included the fishing effort, number and mesh size of nets fished and the type of boat used for the operations. This information was supplemented by total counts of fishermen and of nets throughout the whole fishery at least once each year. The final picture was completed by measuring the "export" from the fishery to the markets farther inland, and this was obtained from the fish levy records of the Tonga Native Authority.

HYDROLOGICAL CONDITIONS IN LAKE KARIBA

Kariba is situated on the boundary between Zambia and Rhodesia between longitudes 27° E. and 29° E. and latitudes 16° 13′ S. and 18° S., lying well within the tropics and at a comparatively low altitude in relation to the rest of the Central African plateau. All of the major rivers which make up the vast watershed of the Zambezi, except the Kafue and Hunyani rivers, drain from the plateau into Lake Kariba, and during an ordinary rainy season approximately one-quarter of the water in the lake is replaced annually. This huge volume of water makes Kariba unique hydrobiologically when compared with the natural lakes of Africa, for despite the low concentration of dissolved salts and moderate silt load, Kariba's massive inflow will be constantly adding new materials which will most likely help to maintain a high level of biological productivity. The climate of this region of Africa affects the hydrology of the lake—this has been described in an earlier paper but for convenience the facts are repeated here.

The meteorological year can be divided into a hot season, from October to March, and a cold season, from April to September. The main rainy period is between January and March, but is often preceded by minor rains in November and December. Winds associated with the hot season are the warm, moist and variable north or north-westerlies while the cold season is characterized by the cold south-east trade winds which blow strongly for long periods along the lake. Rainfall over the lake is only moderate, varying between 16 and 32 in. per annum, but it is very heavy in the upper Zambezi catchment where the average is from 32 to 64 in. per annum.

The initial lake-rise which took full advantage of the 1958–59 rainy season, was roughly 180 ft in the first 6 months of flooding. By January 1960 the level had reached 1 470 ft above sea level and the lake was then nearly 350 ft deep at the dam wall. Thereafter the rise was more gradual and the highest level reached in July 1963 was 1 599 ft a.s.l. This was above the normal operating level of 1 590 ft a.s.l. the level attained following the 1963–64 floods.

Fluctuations in the lake level will in future years be controlled by power requirements, but the annual draw-down should never exceed 10 ft below the maximum level attained in any one season.

Stratification was first recorded in November 1959 when the first temperature profiles were taken in the newly formed lake near the dam wall, and a well-developed thermocline was evident at approximately 10 m. In February 1960 this thermocline was still well developed and records of dissolved oxygen distribution in the water column at this station showed that only the epilimnion contained oxygen. This was also the case at several widely separated sampling stations throughout the lake where the depth exceeded 10 m. Oxygen was only found below the 10 m level in the shallow exposed bays and in these cases thermal stratification was also indistinct.

Temperature profiles taken during the period November 1959 to June 1964 indicate that a definite pattern of thermal stratification had been set from the early days of the lake's formation and may have dated back to the initial flooding early in 1959. Records show no distinct thermocline at that time; but since the recording technique was more precise after November 1959 and since only a few records were taken early in that year, no definite conclusion could be drawn from the data available.

Temperature measurements made within this period showed that the lake was thermally stratified during the hottest months of each year, and that under well-developed thermoclines the hypolimnion was devoid of oxygen for at least a part of each period of stratification. During the period of cooling associated with the rains and the colder part of each year, the thermoclines moved to greater depths and under the influence of the south-east trade winds stratification eventually broke down and the lake overturned. Shortly after this circulation, dissolved oxygen was found to penetrate to the bottom of the lake.

In 1960 the overturn occurred in early July, and the water was homo-
thermal at 23·5°C, cooling continued throughout July and reached a
temperature slightly lower than 21·5°C by the end of August. Warming
of the surface water began in early September, and in November stratification was once again well established, although oxygen persisted below
the thermocline until mid-December of that year.

This pattern of events has been repeated in each successive year; the
variation from the 1960 sequence has only been in the timing, and is
dependent on the precise nature of the annual meteorological changes
(Fig. 1).

Estimates of dissolved oxygen below the thermocline between 1960 and
1964 showed that the period of deoxygenation was shorter in each
successive year. This may be related to a gradual decline in the productivity of the lake water, as it is a measure of biological activity in the
hypolimnion (Fig. 2).

Flooding of the Zambezi valley resulted in the solution of vast quantities of inorganic and organic nutrients leached from the valley soils,
from the decay of rooted vegetation and from the ash of the many trees
burned on the "bush-cleared" areas. This resulted in a highly productive
lake water as exemplified by the appearance of vast plankton blooms, the
explosive growth of water plants such as *Salvinia auriculata*, *Pistia
stratiotes* and the phenomenal increase in the fish population.

This build-up and decline in productivity may be seen best from the
chemical analyses of surface water. These indicated a change from the
riverine condition, where total dissolved salts accounted for 26 p.p.m. at
high water in June 1950 (the only available record of total chemical
analysis before the dam was formed), to 67 p.p.m. at a low water period
in October 1958 just prior to filling, and 65 p.p.m. in December 1958 just
after the closure. These data show a gradual decline after the first
years of flooding to 42 p.p.m. in December 1964. This decline will probably continue until the lake water takes on the chemical characteristics
of the combined inflows with but little influence from bottom deposits,
and future productivity will depend largely on the affluent rivers (Tables
I and II).

FISH AND FISHERIES OF LAKE KARIBA

Studies on the fish and fisheries of the middle Zambezi River were
started in 1955 and were continued throughout the period of filling.

The fauna of this area of the middle Zambezi is isolated from the lower
river by the Kebrabass rapids, from the Upper Zambezi by the Victoria
Falls, and from the fish fauna of minor tributaries by similar geographical
barriers. Only twenty-nine species of fish were found in this area of the

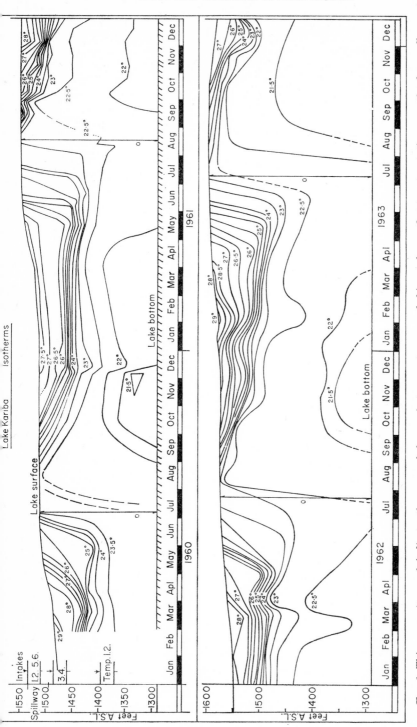

FIG. 1. This composite graph indicates the seasonal changes in temperature recorded in a column of water at a station near the dam wall. Isotherms have been plotted in relation to rising water level and the scale given is the height above sea level in feet from a zero datum at Beira in Portuguese East Africa. The vertical lines labelled "0" indicate the approximate date on which "overturn" of lake water occurred at this station. The positions of the intakes to the turbines and the submerged flood control gates are also indicated.

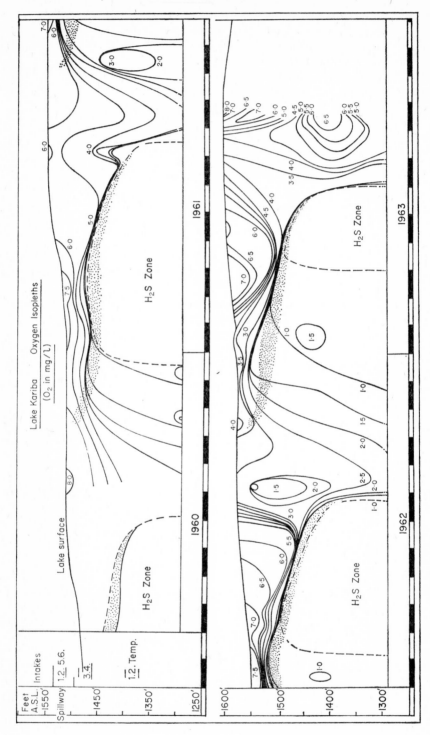

FIG. 2. This diagram indicates the oxygen isopleths plotted on the same depth and times scale as the isotherms in Fig. 1 and at the same station in Lake Kariba. The position of the thermocline throughout the sampling period is indicated by the dotted band.

TABLE I

Chemical Analyses of Surface Water from the Open Water of Lake Kariba near the Dam Site

October samples	1958	1959	1960	1961	1962	1963	1964
Total solid dried at 180°C	103	74	69	64	68	66	53
Loss of wt on ignition	25	15	9	13	8	16	10
Specific conductivity at 20°C ($\times 10^4$)	1·21	1·00	0·93	0·84	0·82	0·76	0·76
Dissolved salines from conductivity	69	58	52	47	46	44	42
Total hardness (as $CaCo_3$ p.p.m.)	49	45	42	39	38	35	35
Chloride	3	2	1	1	1	1	1
Sulphate	3	2·5	Nil	Nil	Nil	Nil	TR
Nitrate-nitrogen	Nil	Nil	Nil	Nil	0·1	0·2	Nil
Nitrite-nitrogen	Nil	Nil	Nil	Nil	Nil	Nil	Nil
Ammoniacal-nitrogen	0·06	0·05	0·06	0·04	0·05	0·05	0·04
Albuminoid-nitrogen	0·26	0·21	0·13	0·07	0·10	0·07	0·09
Bicarbonate	72	66	62	54	52	50	49
Calcium	14	14	13	11	12	10	9
Magnesium	3·6	3·0	2·0	2·0	2·0	2·0	3·0
Total iron	Not detected			3·1	Not detected		
Sodium	8	7	5	3	2	3	2
Potassium	Not done				1·9	1·6	1·6
Silica (SiO_2)	20	16	22	10	15	9	10
pH	7·3	7·2	7·2	7·4	7·4	7·5	7·4
Oxygen absorbed test 4 h at 27°C	1·2	1·8	1·6	1·3	1·15	1·1	0·75
Total dissolved salines from main combinations	67	60	52	45	46	42	41

river compared with ninety from the whole Zambezi system, and of these only nine species have proved to be of importance in the fishery of Lake Kariba (Table III).

The first gill net catches in the Zambezi River prior to inundation indicated that a virgin fishery existed with an abundance of several species of commercially exploitable species, the most important being two species of *Labeo*, two species of *Distichodus*, *Hydrocyon vittatus* and the larger cichlids. Standard fleets of experimental gill nets gave variable catches,

the highest being recorded during the high water period of 1956, in back-
waters off the main river. For example, a 5 in. gill net produced 275 lb fish
for 100 yd of set net. The 5 in. mesh gave consistently high catches by
weight in the River Zambezi, averaging 96 lb/100 yd, while the next best
was the 4 in. mesh which averaged 59 lb/100 yd. The species most frequently caught were *L. congoro*, *L. altivelis* and *H. vittatus*, while *Tilapia
mossambica* often gave high catches in certain localities. Furthermore, the
regime of the river—a period of high water when the banks overflowed
flooding the surrounding country to the depth of several feet, followed by

TABLE II

*Variation in Dissolved Salines, Conductivity and Total Solids in the
Zambezi River and Lake Kariba*

Date	Total solids dried at 180°C	Total solids ignited	Loss on ignition	Specific conductivity	Dissolved salines
21.vi.50	60	47	13	0·46	26
1.xii.55	92(21·5)	—	—	—	—
24.x.58	103	78	25	1·21	69
15.xii.58	91	77	14	1·16	66
11.vi.59	84	69	15	1·15	65
23.xi.59	71	55	16	0·91	52
11.iv.60	70	51	19	0·88	51
31.viii.60	69	60	9	0·93	52
18.vi.61	88	50	38	0·87	48
12.xii.61	66(12)	53	13	0·82	46
6.vi.62	69(2)	61	8	0·80	46
11.xii.62	60(3)	51	9	0·73	42
10.vi.63	60(3)	50	10	0·75	43
25.xi.63	64(3)	52	12	0·77	41
23.vi.64	53(2)	38	15	0·73	40
7.xii.64	54(2)	46	8	0·75	42

a low water period when the river was reduced to a mere trickle between
high banks—had profound effects upon the biology, ecology and abundance of the different species of fish. Most fish species were adapted to
breed on the rising flood thus allowing juveniles to take full advantage of
the flooded river banks for feeding while protected from predation.
Growth of juveniles at this favourable period was extremely rapid and
was followed by slower growth and high mortality during the annual
period of low water. Predation pressure from the ferocious tiger fish (*H.
vittatus*) and other predators had a decisive effect on the whole fauna.
Only those fish which grew to a large size when adult and therefore beyond

the size where predation was effective, were successful in the river, while fish which grew to a small size when adults were strikingly absent.

These preliminary investigations in the river before inundation allowed certain recommendations to be made for improving the fishery of the future lake. First amongst these was the decision to clear large tracts of bush in the future lake basin. Secondly to introduce *Tilapia macrochir*, an important commercial fish in other Central African fisheries, to boost the cichlid stocks in the new lake. Finally a 3-month closed season was recommended from December to March each year to protect the fish during their main breeding migrations.

TABLE III

List of Fishes from the Middle Zambezi and Lake Kariba

Anguilla labiata	*Aplocheilichthys johnstonii*
Protopterus annectens	*Chiloglanis neumanni*
Mormyrus longirostris	*Leptoglanis rotundiceps*
Mormyrops deliciosus	*Eutropius depressirostris*
Marcusenius discorhyncus	*Synodontis zambesensis*
Alestes imberi	*Synodontis nebulosus*
Alestes lateralis	*Clarias mossambicus**
Micralestes acutidens	*Heterobranchus longifilis*
*Hydrocyon vittatus**	*Malapterurus electricus*
*Distichodus mossambicus**	*Tilapia mossambica**
*Distichodus schenga**	*Tilapia melanopleura**
*Labeo altivelis**	*Sargochromis codringtoni**
*Labeo congoro**	*Haplochromis darlingi*
Barbus marequensis	Introduced to the lake:
Barbus barotseensis	*Tilapia macrochir*
Barbus fasciolatus	New record 1964:
Barbus spp.†	*Gnathonemus macrolepidotus*
Barilius zambesensis	

*Fish of commercial importance in Lake Kariba.
† At least four small *Barbus* of uncertain identity.

The change from riverine to lacustrine conditions which began before the main rainy season in 1958–59 proved of benefit to the entire fish population of the future lake. The fish were not subjected to the unfavourable overcrowding of the river at periods of low water, and this resulted in a high survival rate among juveniles, which led in later years to an overall expansion in the total population of the lake.

Catches by experimental fleets of gill nets indicated a continuous high rate of production in 1959 and 1960, but this gradually fell away as commercial fishing developed.

Commercial fisheries started on the north bank of the lake in mid-1960 when Tonga fishermen using gill nets caught about 500 short tons of fish. In 1961 full scale commercial fishing operations had a pronounced effect on the north bank fish populations, and the catch per unit of effort declined rapidly. The average catches of experimental fleets of gill nets ranged from 39 to 83 lb/100 yd of fishing net in 1959 and 1960, varying with the season and location. In 1961 the average catch of experimental nets in the Simamba area of the lake, where there was a well-organized commercial fishery, fell to 14 lb/100 yd, compared with a similar area on the south bank, where no commercial fishery was allowed and a high rate of catching was maintained, the average here being 39 lb/100 yd from a similar fleet of nets. This downward trend in catch per net continued to be reflected in the catches from experimental gill nets in all areas subjected to commercial exploitation in all subsequent years.

However, the commercial fishery on the north bank of the lake has shown a steady increase in overall production since 1960. The highest estimate of production was in excess of 3 500 tons in 1963. It must, however, be remembered that the lake is still settling down and that productivity may fall to an even lower level than it was initially and that figures at present available should not be relied upon as a guide to the final sustained yield of the future Lake Kariba.

The relative importance of Kariba fish to the markets of Zambia can be seen in the most recently published statistics from the north bank of the lake.

"Exports" to the markets in Zambia and Rhodesia were 492 tons in 1960, 1 605 tons in 1961, 2 408 in 1962 and 1 720 tons in 1963, and are based on the fish levy records of the Tonga Native Authority. A large proportion of this levy which amounted to £4 716 in 1963, was used to provide facilities such as fish markets and ferries for the fishing community (Table IV).

TABLE IV

Fish Production* in Zambia

Date	Mweru/ Luapula	Mweru/wa Ntipa	Bangweulu	L. Tangan- yika	Kafue	Kariba N. bank	Total
1959	7 389	864	6 912	2 971	4 900	Nil	23 036
1960	7 306	1 282	6 580	2 943	2 705	500	21 316
1961	6 501	1 700	6 040	2 000	4 337	2 000	22 578
1962	5 598	652	6 400	2 076	6 218	3 000	23 944
1963	6 196	451	6 395	6 900	7 758	3 783	31 483

*Short tons. 1 short ton = 2 000 lb.

Catches from the two large European-controlled enterprises on the south bank of the lake (these started operations in 1963) are not known, since no records were kept, and it has not been possible to give an estimate of production of this area of the lake.

The lake fishery has been based largely on three species of fish, *L. congoro*, *L. altivelis* and *T. mossambica* with the two species of *Distichodus*, *Sargochromis codringtoni*, and *H. vittatus* and the catfish *Clarias mossambicus* making up the rest of the catch. In 1962 the average commercial landings from the four main fishing areas on the north bank consisted of 35% *T. mossambica*, 20·5% *L. altivelis* and 21·5 % *L. congoro* out of a total of eighteen species recorded (Table V).

TABLE V

The Proportions of Different Fish Species (% Numbers) in the Commercial Landings on the North Bank of Lake Kariba 1962

	Simamba	Chipepo	Sinazongwe	Mwemba	Total
Labeo altivelis	42·14	18·79	15·57	7·94	20·57
Labeo congoro	32·10	27·27	16·13	10·47	21·56
Tilapia mossambica	5·07	29·32	44·32	67·01	35·07
Other species	20·69	24·62	23·98	4·58	22·70
Total no. of fish caught	25 927	397 367	726 828	100 607	1 470 162
Total weight of fish caught (lb)	518 244	902 680	1 826 576	239 191	3 486 691
Average catch (lb/100 yd)	38·52	35·84	46·52	42·40	

Tilapia macrochir which had been stocked at the rate of approximately 7 tons of fingerlings per annum between 1959 and 1962 continued to appear in the commercial catches, but only in very small numbers. This suggests that the introduction was only partly successful. It must, however, be borne in mind that the breeding potential of the naturally occurring fish population was far in excess of that of the introduced species, and was immediately effective. *T. macrochir* fingerlings would not have reached breeding size before 1963 and could not be expected to have much effect on the population unless this breeding and all subsequent breedings were successful.

The story of the formation of Lake Kariba would be incomplete without reference to the water fern *Salvinia auriculata*. The "explosive" growth of this plant has already been mentioned, but it became one of the more spectacular and perhaps even menacing features of the lake.

Floating mats of the weed were first seen in August 1959 and by the end of the year it covered roughly 150 square miles of the lake area. The maximum growth occurred in 1962 when close to 250 square miles of the lake surface were covered by the weed. After this it began to decline. In many areas a "sudd" developed due to the growth of semi-aquatics, such as *Scirpus cubensis*, on the floating mats of *Salvinia*. These "sudd" patches were originally found to be associated with semi-submerged trees but later they blocked many back waters and river estuaries. This became a hazard to navigation, made fishing difficult and even curtailed all fishing activities in some areas.

However, once the cleared sections were flooded the mats of weed soon broke up under wave and wind action, and today the infected areas are confined to those regions where bush clearing was not carried out, where semi-submerged trees are abundant and in most river estuaries and bays. Thus bush clearing proved its worth not only to the fishery but also as an effective control to the spread of *Salvinia*.

CONCLUSIONS

Data presented here summarize briefly the changes which took place between 1956 and 1964 in the Zambezi River and Lake Kariba.

From these studies it is obvious that a great deal of valuable information was not obtained in the crucial period of the first year of flooding, and indeed before the dam was actually formed.

Any future dam project should, if possible, be preceded by long-term investigation of the limnology and ecology of the river system above and in the area to be flooded, and should include detailed studies on the populations and biology of fish. These researches should be maintained continuously throughout the critical period of initial flooding, and thereafter a continuous check should be kept on the hydrology and the fish population of the lake.

Under no circumstances should new species be introduced to the newly forming lake until a better understanding of the fish population in the new lake is obtained.

Money should also be spent in clearing trees and shrubs from the shallow margins of the lake since clearing has been proved worthwhile both to the fishery, by facilitating the operation of nets, and in keeping the lake free from *Salvinia auriculata* and other floating debris. Beaches also form more rapidly on these cleared shores and consequently can be developed for tourism.

Where, as in the Zambezi valley, the rehabilitation of a pastoral people may have to be taken into account, arrangements should be made at an early stage to train a proportion of these people to exploit the fisheries likely to develop in the lake. The Fisheries Training School in Zambia may be taken as an excellent model for any future schemes envisaged in Africa.

Discussion

WORTHINGTON: Kariba demonstrates the huge biological changes and fantastic fish potential in early years after inundation. Harding took me to see gill nets lifted from Kariba in 1962, and though I have been used to seeing large catches from virgin lakes I was quite staggered by the fantastic returns at the height of productivity here. It has now gone down a lot, but whether it has reached a steady state remains to be seen.

YONGE: What is happening on the south bank?

HARDING: Conditions on the south bank were different in that the original decision to close this section of the lake to all commercial fishing was rigidly enforced for three years. The recommendation was made in the first instance for the whole lake in order to protect the introduced *Tilapia macrochir* and to allow what were considered small river stocks to build up in the early stages of the development of Lake Kariba. It was obvious after the first year that such drastic steps to protect fish stocks were unnecessary and the closed fishing season was therefore introduced in 1960 for the months when peak breeding took place. This was only adopted on the north bank of the lake. Commercial fishing only began in the latter part of 1962 on the south bank and few records have been made available. The only detailed records come from experimental gill nets which were fished from 1959 onwards, while records of the commercial catch were available from late 1963, but merely related to "exports" from the lake. The main feature of the south bank fishery was that exploitation was mainly in the hands of two highly organized large commercial firms and only in 1964 did an African peasant fishery develop. By 1965 this was so successful that the commercial firms largely discontinued their fishing effort and concentrated on buying fish from the numerous small-scale African operators.

McCONNELL: Can Mr. Harding give an estimate of the area of the lake which is actually fished to produce these tonnages?

HARDING: It is not possible to give this at the moment because I have not worked out a figure. The lake was rarely fished to depths greater than 60 ft, and the area would probably be that bounded by the offshore contour of 60 ft in depth. However, *Salvinia* would exclude a large and variable portion of inshore waters to fishery.

MORGAN: To what extent was the high production of fish, after Kariba was flooded, due to heavy feeding on terrestrial invertebrates drowned as the level of the lake rose, or were the fish feeding chiefly on aquatic organisms?

HARDING: Terrestrial invertebrates and plants were only utilized by the fish as food in the very early stages of flooding. Fish were found to be feeding

B

mainly on aquatic organisms, chiefly zooplankton and phytoplankton but also on other aquatic organisms living, for example, among the roots of *Salvinia*. *Salvinia* was also utilized by at least two fish species.

HAIGH: Have biologists made correlations between fish population and salt content in lakes? If such correlations are possible, then it might be practicable to make a forecast of the long-term production of the industry at Kariba from chemical analysis of the river before the lake was impounded, assuming that the salinity in the lake would eventually return to that level. Has a forecast on these lines been attempted?

HARDING: No. I doubt whether enough data are available on which such estimates could be based. Correlations between production of lakes and available chemicals in the lake and their catchments have been attempted but only after long-term studies on fauna, flora and chemistry of the lake water. This type of information is not available from Kariba.

Biological Investigations on the Volta Lake
May 1964 to May 1965

D. W. EWER

Volta Basin Research Project, University of Ghana, Accra, Ghana

As early as 1915 a proposal was put forward to dam the Volta River as a source of hydro-electric power for Ghana. A serious examination of this proposal was initiated in 1952 and work upon the scheme was finally started in 1962, nearly five years after the country had become independent. In May 1964 the dam was closed and the formation of the Volta Lake began. After a year the lake level has risen so that at its deepest point there is now about 50 m of water. At maximal flooding this depth will be about 70 m. The lake will have a complex dendritic shape with a main basin along the old Volta River but with a major arm running westward along the course of the Afram and, at the head of the lake, a long narrowing reach running north-west towards the confluence of the Black and White Voltas. The total area of the lake will cover more than 3 000 square miles and the shore line will exceed 4 500 miles in length.

As in other such projects official interest has centred around the industrial potential of the hydro-electric scheme and no proposals for a scientific study of the lake as such were made until about a year before closure of the dam. At that time the University of Ghana set up an organization, the Volta Basin Research Project, primarily to co-ordinate the work of University Departments interested in problems within the Volta Basin. A diversity of talents was represented—archaeology, history, geography, geology, the study of religions, economics, sociology and also biology.

The biological work started with a survey of the zooplankton as well as of the water weeds in the river basin. Somewhat later studies on the phytoplankton, together with observations upon the water chemistry, were initiated. For various reasons adequate financial provision for biological studies could not be made until the end of 1963. One result of this has been that a vessel suitable for work over so wide an area has only just become available and observations during the first year after closure of the dam have been largely restricted to an intensive study of an area close to the dam site. This may prove to be atypical of the main water body,

21

although limited sampling suggests that the general picture which has emerged is probably broadly valid.

With the experience of Kariba in mind, one of the first problems which arose was whether there were any steps which should be taken before flooding which might reduce the danger of sudd formation by weeds. At the same time a full clearance programme was considered, both to facilitate fisheries and to eliminate a possible threat of extensive deoxygenation owing to the rotting of flooded vegetation. It became clear that such an undertaking was financially prohibitive, nor was it possible to prevail upon the inhabitants to fell trees for timber as the lack of road development in the area made it impossible to transport the trunks economically to any centre. More recently two areas of the lake, as yet unflooded and adjacent to agricultural settlements, have been cleared of all vegetation to facilitate gill net and seine net fishing, as well as being of use later in possible trials on the value of bottom fishing techniques. The annual draw off will further expose large areas of shore which can presently be cleared if this should prove to be of value. The possibility of extensive burning to reduce the load of vegetation which would have to decompose was also considered, but finally rejected on the grounds that this might lead to a situation in which the first flood waters were greatly enriched with nutrients. It was suggested that this might lead to the danger of a weed explosion and that, while a loss of fish from deoxygenation of the water might be serious, it was not likely to prove as irreversible as the development of very extensive weed beds.

In the event there has, so far at least, been no formation of a weed sudd. During the early months both *Lemna* and *Pistia* were abundant while *Ceratophyllum*, floating freely just below the lake surface, appeared in gradually increasing quantity. At the present time *Ceratophyllum* is common and scattered beds of *Pistia* occur, particularly along the eastern shore where they provide shelter for young *Tilapia* and *Hemichromis* which partly feed among the roots. The absence of any serious growth of water-weed on the Volta Lake is in keeping with the suggestion that the outburst of *Salvinia* on Kariba was due to the fact that it was an exotic. This, however, does imply that there is considerable need for a close guard upon possible sources of infestation, especially from small streams. It is intended to complete a survey of water weeds within the Volta Basin inside Ghana in the near future; but the lake draws water from neighbouring territories and we have been unable to find reports of any surveys in these regions. When the Ghanaian survey is completed, it is hoped that we may be able to extend this to both Upper Volta and Togo. Meanwhile posters have been printed in some eight different languages showing papyrus, *Eichhornia* and *Salvinia*, and asking anyone who sees plants

which they believe to tally with these pictures to inform the relevant
authorities immediately.

While we had foreseen the possibility of some deoxygenation, the extent and above all the speed with which this developed after the closure of
the dam came as a surprise. A routine sampling station had been established in mid-stream of the river about a mile north of the dam site and
here observations were made weekly upon the chemistry of the water and
on the phytoplankton density. The river water at this station was always
well saturated with oxygen and at the time of closure of the dam there
was a very extensive water bloom. Immediately after the dam was closed
the oxygen concentration at the surface was found to be more than 300%
saturated. Within four weeks the level of oxygen in the surface layer had
dropped to 16% saturation, while almost no oxygen was found at 10 m
(Fig. 1).

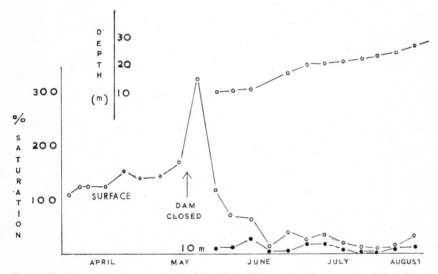

FIG. 1. Variation in oxygen content of the Volta River and subsequently of the lake at
the surface and at a depth of 10 m during 1964. Upper curve shows the depth of the lake
at succeeding weekly observations.

In the subsequent months the mean level of oxygen at the surface has
remained low, the deeper water being very poorly oxygenated. The oxygenated layer is usually limited to the upper 5 m and at 10 m has exceeded
10% saturation only on rare occasions (Fig. 2). This poor oxygenation is
in part attributable to the turbidity of the water which limits photosynthesis. The Secchi disk has normally read about 1m, while light penetration measurements at different wavelengths give extinction coefficients

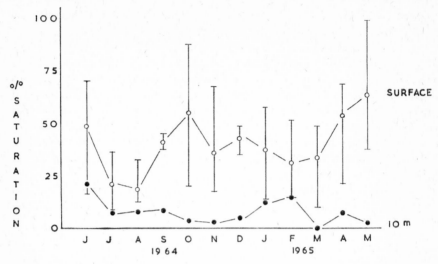

FIG. 2. Mean monthly oxygen content of the Volta Lake at Adjena at the surface and at
10 m. Observations were made weekly. Vertical bars indicate the spread between the
highest and lowest oxygen values of the surface water recorded each month.

through 1 m of 0·70 or more, red light penetrating considerably farther
than blue or green. Nevertheless the extent of the oxygenation of the
surface layer shows some correlation with the density of the phytoplankton (Biswas, 1966). Its most characteristic feature, however, is its
variability, which can be seen by the very wide limits of upper and lower
values recorded each month (Fig. 2). This variability is probably largely
due to isothermal mixing of the surface layers. This is illustrated in Fig. 3
where a series of oxygen and temperature profiles taken at 2-hourly
intervals shows both the shallowness of the oxygenated layer and also a
sudden fall in the level of oxygenation between successive readings when
the surface temperature fell.

In our initial thinking about the lake we had assumed, by analogy
with limited measurements upon Lake Busomtwi, that there would be a
thermocline at about 20 m and a well oxygenated epilimnion. We were
therefore concerned whether a major turnover would occur, leading to
extensive fish mortality. Since no very drastic changes in water temperature were to be expected, we felt that such a turnover would be an
unlikely happening. Both these expectations have been belied in the
event. Normally, apart from transient daily heating of the most superfi-
cial layer, there is no thermocline. Temperature falls gradually until
about 25 m; below this the temperature is almost uniform. The water
does show a reasonably clear-cut division into a surface layer reaching

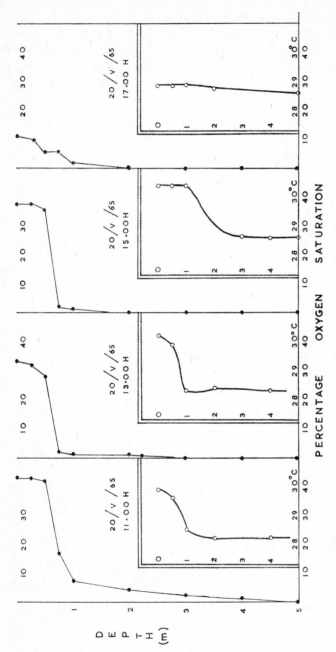

Fig. 3. Oxygen and temperature depth profiles taken at 2-hourly intervals at Adjena. Note that the depth scales for the two parameters are different.

down to about 10 m, then a transitional layer extending to about
25 m and finally a fairly uniform bottom layer. This layering shows up
markedly both in the ammonia content of the water and in the total iron,
and also, but less distinctly, in the phosphate (Fig. 4). It is recognizably
reflected as well in pH, alkalinity and in potassium.

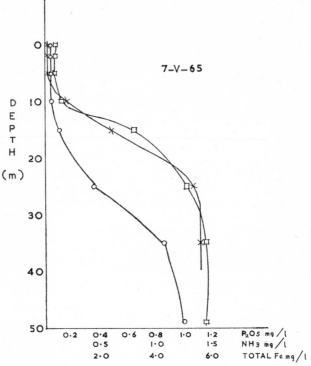

FIG. 4. Depth profiles of total iron (□), ammonia (×) and phosphate (○) at Adjena.

Experience suggests that total iron is a particularly sensitive indicator
of bulk water movements. Thus, while the value of the total iron in the
upper waters in usually less than 0·5 mg/l and frequently less than 0·2
mg/l, in March 1965 it rose as high as 1·44 mg/l, a value not normally
found above 25 m depth. At the same time the oxygen saturation at a
depth of 1 m was only 1% and below this there was none. Such a result
suggests that there had been very extensive vertical mixing, but we have
yet to learn the cause of this type of event. We do, however, know that
this was not something peculiar to the station close to the dam, as similar
observations on oxygen content were made at the same time about 13
miles farther north.

Our observations indicate that, at least at its present level, the lake is very unstable and that, if conditions at our sampling station are indeed typical, low oxygen concentrations are likely to persist for a considerable time. Thus the picture of the hydrology of the Volta Lake is very different from that of Lake Kariba. In Kariba a very sharply demarcated thermocline is established during the cooler months at a depth of about 30 m. No such thermocline is found in the Volta (Fig. 5). As a result the lower layers of decaying vegetation have at no time been sealed off from the upper waters and the whole is relatively free to mix. This mixing contributes, at least in part, to the high turbidity of the water. As a consequence light penetration is poor, so that there is only a very shallow zone of photosynthetic activity. It remains to be seen whether or not a definite thermocline will be established when the lake is completely filled.

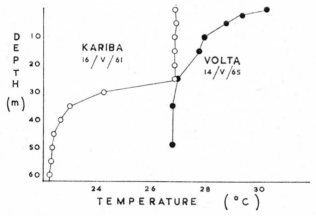

FIG. 5. Temperature depth profiles from Lakes Kariba and Volta. Data for Lake Kariba taken from Report No. 11 (1961) of the Joint Fisheries Research Organization of the Governments of Northern Rhodesia and Nyasaland.

The next point worthy of discussion is the distribution of the bottom fauna. Here investigations have been started only recently. They show that the bottom fauna spreads down from the lake shore to a depth of about 4 or 5 m; that is it spreads about as far as the lower level of oxygen. Below this there is nothing. So far there is no sign of any invasion of organisms capable of existing in the deeper anaerobic water. This distribution of the fauna resembles that which has been found in the upper reaches of the Volta River where the main production of benthos in the dry season, excluding areas of rapids, is a narrow strip extending to 2 or 3 m depth. In this case, however, oxygen is certainly not a limiting factor.

B*

A study of the productivity of the lake in terms of fish caught has very recently been initiated by the Fisheries Inspectorate Unit of the Ghana Government, but there is as yet no estimate of total catch and it is likely to be some considerable time before such figures can be obtained. Although there is reason to believe that the fishery is somewhat more productive than was that of the river, there have been no indications of any miraculous draught of fishes. Clearly it will be necessary to wait some years to see whether the changed conditions lead to a greater survival of fish fry. Certainly the initial deoxygenation led to the death of a variety of fishes; now at the station adjacent to the dam only *Chrysichthys* is to be found floating on the surface from time to time. But this may well be a reflection of special conditions which arise close to the dam itself.

Gill nettings with nets of different mesh have been made about 3 miles north of the dam site. The two smaller mesh nets of 1½ and 2 in. predominantly catch *Alestes* spp., *Chrysichthys*, *Hydrocynus* and *Lates*. We have been able to examine the stomach contents of a limited number of these fishes. *Alestes* appears to be essentially a shore-line feeder with a very variable diet, while *Chrysichthys* feeds chiefly upon chironomids, that is to say also in shallow water. *Hydrocynus* and *Lates* are predatory upon other fishes. In 3 in. nets the dominant catch has been *Labeo senegalensis* and *L. coubie*. The former appears to be a detritus feeder and the latter to be feeding on the *Aufwuchs*; both again are essentially shore-line feeders. *Synodontis* spp. are also caught in these nets; their stomach contents show them to be feeding largely on chironomids and *Aufwuchs* but they may also feed on plankton as well as the leaves of higher plants. Finally in the 4 in. nets the more numerous fish are *Clarias* spp. Their stomach contents reflect their very omnivorous diet which may include other fishes. It will be noted that, apart from the predators and *Clarias*, these animals are feeding either exclusively or at least to a great extent on the inshore fauna and flora. This is perhaps to be expected since their former feeding grounds were probably the shore-lines of the river and the fish have, so to speak, moved with the shores as these have moved due to the filling of the lake. In this connexion it is to be noted that the *Ceratophyllum* floating off-shore supports a population of typically shore-living forms and is probably a subsidiary feeding ground for some of these fishes.

Detailed examination of the zooplankton shows the species living in the open water to be different from those close in to the shore. This is to be expected. The species found are mostly widespread and, as far as they have been worked out, all were present in the Volta Basin before the lake started to form. The picture with the phytoplankton is very similar. With one exception all the species encountered in the lake also occurred in the river. The exception is *Pediastrum simplex* which, although common in the river, has not been taken since the lake was formed.

There is one obvious question which I cannot answer, namely "what of possible vectors of disease?" No systematic survey specifically concerned with this problem has been undertaken.

Finally it is not enough to consider the formation of the lake and the damming of the river without some remarks on the situation downstream from the dam. Below the dam the Volta runs for a matter of about 60 miles before reaching the sea. The lower reaches are estuarine and have, in the past, supported a large fishing industry based upon the seasonal flooding of extensive ponds and creeks along the sides of the river, as well as a fishery for the clam, *Egeria*, which is of economic importance to the area.

The closure of the dam has drastically reduced the flow of fresh water into the lower Volta and as a result the tidal run now reaches farther up river than before. Furthermore the water being discharged into the river at the present time is drawn off through a tunnel at the base of the dam. Knowing the extensive decomposition taking place on the lake floor, there was some anxiety lest the outflow of foul water might have serious repercussions on the economy of the lower Volta. Certainly the water emerging from the outflow tunnel is malodorous and devoid of oxygen.

The fate of the clam fisheries has been closely watched as *Egeria* does not occur in the other estuaries of Ghana or of the neighbouring countries. It will not survive in sea water and its destruction would constitute a serious economic loss to the inhabitants of the lower Volta. Since late in 1964 the water-flow into the river has been very low and there are indications that the resulting high salinities have had an adverse effect upon the clams. Nevertheless they have survived and, since they are now known to grow very rapidly, it is reasonable to expect that once the turbines come into action the situation will be corrected and the clams will rapidly reestablish themselves.

The fisheries in the lower river present a different problem for they have depended in the past upon seasonal flooding. In August 1963 there were tremendous floods and these together with subsequent rains have maintained the creeks up to the present time. But clearly once the full water-flow is established the problems of the fisheries in this area will require a new approach, as there will be no annual change of level unless there are very exceptional floods. Studies on methods of fish pond farming are proceeding in this region and it seems likely that, if these are successful, productive fisheries unaffected by the vagaries of flood levels will be established.

To sum up our present findings, it appears, within the limits of our knowledge, that the Volta Lake at present is a physically, and therefore chemically, unstable water mass characterized by a highly variable level of oxygenation which does not penetrate significantly below 10 m. Biologically it may be regarded both as a vastly broad river, with the fish still living, predominantly, on the shore lines and, from the viewpoint of the plankton, as a large pond. This admittedly is a caricature, but we have yet to learn how far the greatly increased water mass may modify the behaviour and general biology of the fauna and whether a distinct flora will presently appear.

ACKNOWLEDGEMENTS

In presenting this picture of research upon the Volta Lake I have been dependent upon the generosity of my colleagues, Dr. S. Biswas, Dr. T. Petr, Dr. Maria Proszynska, Mr. A. B. Viner and Mr. Walter Pople who have allowed me to quote their results and observations. My own role in this undertaking has been little other than that of an administrator and, in the present instance, of a rapporteur. I have great pleasure in expressing my thanks to them and also to the Chief Fisheries Officer for allowing me to include certain data collected by his staff. My thanks and that of my colleagues are also due to the Chief Executive of Volta River Authority and to the Government of Ghana without whose generous support nothing could have been accomplished.

REFERENCE

Biswas, S. (1966). Oxygen and phytoplankton changes in the newly forming Volta Lake in Ghana. *Nature Lond.* **209**, 218–219.

Note added in proof

During the rainy season of July and August 1965, the extent of the *Pistia* beds upon the Volta Lake increased very considerably and, at least in the Afram arm, densely packed mats were formed upon which secondary growth of other plants occurred. Dr. J. D. Thomas (personal communication) has observed that, during the first rainy season, after its formation, the small reservoir at Nungwa near Accra was almost completely covered with *Pistia* which then receded during the following dry season. Each subsequent rainy season has seen renewed growth of the weed, but the area covered at its maximum has decreased with succeeding years. There is therefore the possibility that the infestation upon the Volta Lake may also gradually decrease with time.

Discussion

WORTHINGTON: Could Professor Ewer tell us what his team consists of and what they are working on?

EWER: We have a full-time member of the team studying the phytoplankton and water chemistry, another studying zooplankton mainly from the taxonomic angle at present, another on benthos. In addition to the team, some members of the University staff are working part-time on Volta problems, one studying the important clam fishery below the dam, another on rates at which the submerged timber rots, another on the shore ecology. Our great shortcoming is that we have not yet anyone working on fish.

WADDY: Professor Ewer questions whether any work has been done affecting the Volta outside Ghana. I wonder if he is aware of ORSTOM's work on *Simulium* control higher up the Volta?

EWER: I was really referring to lack of weed studies in the territories upstream.

LITTLE: Can you explain how the deoxygenation below the weed mats has come about?

EWER: There is deoxygenation in the bottom waters where there is no weed, but below the weed mats it comes right to the surface. Even water below *Lemna* will have a reduced oxygen content; *Ceratophyllum*, on the other hand, which floats below the water surface rather like *Sargassum* weed oxygenates the water.

HOLDEN: If no clearing was carried out in Volta how are the nets set?

EWER: Surface nets are used.

STEELE: What sort of bottom fauna is there? Will this persist if it is poorly represented?

EWER: It is really a shore fauna, dominantly of chironomids and *Aufwuchs*; it is presumably from the shore fauna of the river. It should persist unless the weed cover round the shore kills it. But it is limited to the shore. Deep down there is nothing, not even oligochaetes or nematodes.

The Brokopondo Research Project, Surinam*

P. LEENTVAAR

State Institute for Nature Conservation Research (RIVON), Zeist, The Netherlands

In 1963 the Netherlands Foundation for Scientific Research in Surinam and the Netherlands Antilles ("Studiekring"), sent a team of four scientists to Surinam to investigate the biological changes resulting from the building of a dam across the Suriname River. The barrage, completed on 1 February 1964, was built by the Suriname Aluminium Company for hydro-electric purposes. The power-station will yield energy primarily for the conversion of bauxite into aluminium.

The funds for the studies were allocated by the Netherlands Foundation for the Advancement of Research in Surinam and the Netherlands Antilles (Wosuna), and hydrobiological investigations were started in November 1963. In 1954 the "Studiekring" published a study by J. P. Schulz concerning the ecological consequences of building a dam across the Suriname River, by comparing data gathered from literature in different tropical regions.

As few data were known from the Suriname River and the available time for collecting and sampling before the closure of the dam was short, our knowledge of plant and animal life before the changing of the environment is not complete. However, the few trips made on the river before the closing of the dam and regular sampling at Pokigron, which is located south of the future border of the lake, provided sufficient data for comparison.

The Suriname River flows from south to north through tropical rain-forest. The river-bed is composed of rocks and sandflats, which become exposed during periods of low water level. The trees of the forest border the banks directly, and no swampy areas or extensive stretches of stagnant water are found. Several rapids and falls form obstacles to the flow of the water. In the stretches between the falls and rapids the speed of the water slows down and here sedimentation of sand takes place. There is practically no mud on the bottom, since the river carries little silt. During the rainy season the water level rises and the river banks are flooded. Many rapids become submerged and large areas of the bordering forest

*RIVON communication no. 232.

are flooded. Some trees are entirely submerged and this may last for some weeks or even months without harming the trees.

On the bare rocks of the rapids Podostemaceae are found. These are the only water-plants found in the river. Among the Podostemaceae live several organisms adapted to strong currents. Several species of Ephemeroptera, Trichoptera, Simulidae, Odonata, Sialoidea and caterpillars (*Cataclysta*) were collected. Freshwater shrimps (*Macrobrachium*) and crabs are common, but these prefer the quieter parts between the rocks. Crusts of freshwater sponges cover the stones, and freshwater snails of the genera *Pomacea* (*Ampullaria*) and *Doryssa* can be found. In the sand-flats few animals could be found. Freshwater clams (*Diplodon voltzi*) occur in softer bottoms, as are found at the inflow of little streams.

The plankton of the Suriname River was collected weekly at Pokigron. This was also done at Akobaka near the dam. The motile plankters, like copepods, cladocerans, rotifers and flagellates, are very scarce. Diatoms and desmids are dominant. By analogy with plankton communities found in temperate climates, the character of the community indicates oligotrophic conditions.

The colour of the water is turbid brown. As in many rivers of the Amazon region, the Suriname is very poor in minerals and the pH is low. For the Amazon area Sioli (1964) distinguished clear-waters, brown- or black-waters, and white-waters. In Surinam the brown-water type is present in savanna regions, but the Suriname River and also several others do not belong to this type as practically no colouring by dissolved humic acids is present. The colour of the Suriname River is due to iron and silica in suspension, and it has some similarity to the clear-water type of Sioli. I prefer to characterize the Suriname as a turbid-brown water. The white-water type of Sioli is absent in Surinam. In British Guiana, Carter (1934) distinguished white-waters and black-waters. These categories are in general adequate for the rivers in Surinam also, but confusion must be avoided with the different meaning of "white-water" type of both investigators.

Summarizing the character of the Suriname River: it is an acid running water, poor in minerals, turbid-brown in colour, and with a poor development of water-plants and animals, concentrated mainly in the rapids and falls.

In order to understand the situation in the river during a dry period and a rainy period the following must be mentioned. According to weekly observations at Pokigron the water level from December until March is fairly constant. In the last week of May the main rainy season starts and the water level rises about 2 m for a period of 2 months. The temperature shows fluctuations between 25° and 31·5°C. In the dry season the water is warmer and the electrical conductivity is higher. During this period the normal river plankton is developing, with several species (such as *Eunotia asterionelloides, Dictyosphaerium, Gonatozygon*). This community is washed downstream shortly after the beginning of the rains. The species decrease in number and another community with characteristic forms (*Arcella, Heliozoa, Rhipidodendron* and *Fungi imperfecti*) appears from narrow affluents, until during the months of July and August practically pure rain-water flows through the river, except for some detritus and a few spicules of sponges. During a long rainy period the river cleans itself and the river plankton is washed downstream. Therefore at a fixed station we first catch river plankton, after which a community is found washed down from narrow tributaries, and finally at the end of a long period of rain practically no plankton is found. This sequence of events may also occur at Afobaka near the dam in the course of the year, but the closing of the dam on 1 February prevented further observations. Naturally in the stretch from Pokigron to Afobaka some enrichment of the plankton, and also of the mineral content, takes place, which may result in a somewhat less pronounced picture.

After the closing of the dam, the lake began to fill, and the future lake will cover an area of about 1 500 km^2. The depth near the dam will be about 50 m. The yearly rainfall in this region is between 2 000 and 3 000 mm. It was estimated that the lake would reach its final level during the second half of 1965. The observations given here cover the period from November 1963 to September 1964, after which time J. van der Heide of our team continued the investigations.

In the future lake ten sampling stations were planned for weekly examination of oxygen, temperature, pH, electrical conductivity, transparency, depth and plankton. The results of the measurements are discussed from two stations. The first is located near the dam at Afobaka in the former Suriname River; the second is located in the former Sarakreek, a narrow tributary of the Suriname River, and this station represents conditions in an environment shut off from wind in the midst of the forest (see Fig. 1).

Before dam closure the oxygen content was nearly always saturated at the surface. At Afobaka, at first supersaturation was noticed for a short time after closure. This has also been found at other stations after the current had stopped. More will be said about this below. At Sara this supersaturation was not present. Four weeks after dam closure ("stagnation") oxygen was exhausted in the deeper layers, and oxygen was only present in the upper 3–4 m (Fig. 2). This situation remained permanent. After 18 March the decrease in oxygen content at the surface ceased and a restabilization was established. However, below 3–4 m the water

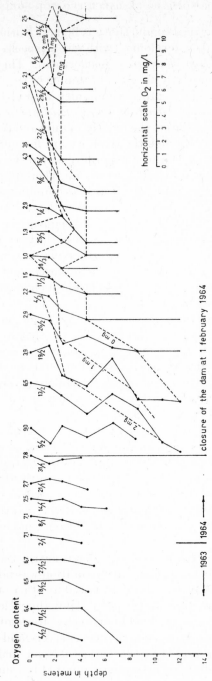

FIG. 2. The depth distribution of dissolved oxygen before and after dam closure, Brokopondo. (Period 4 December 1963 to 13 May 1964; dates signified thus: 4/12 = 4 December etc.)

THE BROKOPONDO RESEARCH PROJECT, SURINAM

remained without oxygen and through the decaying of organic matter
hydrogen sulphide developed. In the Sara environment oxygen was
totally absent from top to bottom for several weeks. After longer stagnation, when the water level rose and the lake area increased, both stations
became similar in environmental conditions.

The temperature in the Sarakreek was always some degrees lower than
that in the Suriname River because of the shade of the trees. After
stagnation the temperature increased at the surface and decreased near
the bottom. After the dry period of April and May a drop in temperature
was caused by rain, but in July values were found as high as 34°C. The
temperature fluctuations from day to day in the 3–4 m layer were very
great.

The electrical conductivity in the shallow meandering Sarakreek was
always higher than in the Suriname River, but soon after stagnation it
dropped to the values found at Afobaka as a result of dilution. At both
stations after the dam closure it increased during dry times and dropped
during the short rainy period on 18 March and during the long period of
rain after 27 May.

The transparency of the water, measured with the Secchi disk, was
about 1·5–2 m in the Suriname River and no more than 1 m in the Sarakreek. After the dam closure it increased through sedimentation and
changes in plankton composition, especially in the Sara region. Later it
remained fairly constant at 1 m, interrupted only by the heavy rains of
27 May.

The pH, which was approximately 6·5 in the running water, dropped
soon after dam closure to values of approximately 5·5. The pH was also
affected temporarily by the rains.

The plankton community of the river water changed after stagnation.
Crustaceans, rotifers and unicellular flagellates developed in great
numbers. They only occurred in the 3–4 m oxygen-containing layer. The
diatom *Eunotia asterionelloides* which is characteristic of the running
river decreased in numbers and *Melosira* increased. Colonies of *Eudorina
elegans* only increased for a short time, during the transitional period,
when the oxygen was not yet stabilized at 3–4 m. This organism also
appeared in great numbers in the unaffected river at the beginning and
the end of rainy periods, when the environment was disturbed. This
species of river plankton may be seen as a component of the self-purification of the water in natural circumstances. After the permanent disturbance, caused by the damming, it decreased in numbers after a short
bloom. During this transitional period the plankton was coloured green
by *Eudorina* and this green wave moved south when the stagnation had
lasted longer. So everywhere in the forming lake a transitional zone

between running and stagnant water was present, with great numbers of *Eudorina*. Also many cladocerans developed at the same time. The transitional environment was followed by the lake environment in which many unicellular flagellates developed (*Trachelomonas, Strombomomas*). They occurred only in the upper 3–4 m in which the daily temperature and oxygen content fluctuations were extreme. The character of this biocommunity is similar to that of swamps. The amount of decaying organic matter, derived from the drowning forest, is high, which is favourable for the development of the organisms mentioned. The swamp character of the plankton already indicates the future botanical development of the lake, as large parts of the future lake will be shallow with dead trees and swamp vegetation.

For a better understanding of the properties of the river water and the processes in the stagnant lake water, I refer to some daily observations.

The daily observations in slow-moving water at Afobaka show that oxygen is nearly saturated from top to bottom. However, the remarkable fact was noticed that the oxygen content in the morning was higher than in the afternoon, especially in the deeper layers. Figure 3 shows the

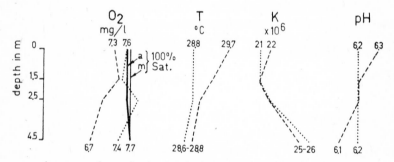

Averages of morning (·····) and afternoon (– – –) values in the Suriname river at Afobaka in the period from 14-23 January 1964

Fɪɢ. 3. Comparison of morning and afternoon values for depth distribution of oxygen (O_2), temperature (T), conductivity (K), and pH, in the Suriname River, January 1964.

averages for morning and afternoon values in January. The temperature was higher in the afternoon, and it may be deduced from the figures that the heat absorption is restricted mainly to the layers above 2·5 or 1·5 m. As it is known that at these high tropical temperatures great differences in density exist in the water, I surmise that the differences in oxygen content are caused by great differences in density. At night the water cools and sinks, carrying oxygen to lower levels. In the morning the surface water is warmed (swiftly) and remains on top, preventing the more saturated deeper water from rising and mixing with the surface water. This is confirmed by the observations after 1 February where super-saturated water was also recorded at depth, and with maxima which must be related to diurnal periodicity. The electrical conductivity and the pH also showed variations. The supersaturation of river water has also been recorded in temperate climates by Schmassmann (1955), Mortimer (1956) and Lindroth (1957) for oligotrophic waters as abiogenic supersaturation.

After long stagnation, in May and July, the oxygen fluctuations were greater than in the former river, and the oxygen content in the afternoon was then higher than in the morning, which is typical for eutrophic waters. In this connexion I surmise that the source of oxygen was biogenic, which is very likely as numerous flagellates were present. However, in BOD dark and light bottles, I could not find convincing records of oxygen overproduction. The almost abiogenic character of the oxygen regime of the river was confirmed by BOD tests. The BOD in the dark values were very low, as was also found by Utermöhl (1958) in lake water in the tropics.

It seems to me that the organic matter present in the water is mineralized swiftly as the temperatures are high, and as a result the amount of organic matter which will be measured is always very low or absent. The intensity of decomposition is very high and probably cannot be measured by normal BOD tests. In this case, where a very low mineral content is present in the water, measurements of the mineralization products by electrical conductivity may be valuable. This was demonstrated in the measurements of electrical conductivity on 20 July, which recorded a morning maximum at 2·5 m depth which decreased and sank down later in the day. This record showed the swift decomposition of organic matter prevailing in the lake.

In this paper no further details will be given of the results found at different sampling stations. The fish fauna is not considered. The ichthyologist of our team, Dr. M. Boeseman, was concerned with this part of the research. The river is rich in species and numbers, mainly predators. After the closing of the dam the first dead fish were found after about 3 weeks. These were bottom dwellers such as the stingray. At Afobaka many dead fish were found on 28 February. The number of fish that died was, however, small in comparison with those which must have been present in the undisturbed river. At the beginning of the rainy season, 13 May, many fish were seen at the surface, but they disappeared again. In August and September great concentrations of fish were seen in the upper reaches of the river. Catfish (*Plecostomus* sp.) which live only in the rapids were several times found floating dead at the surface above the place where a rapid was present in the former river. These fish are strictly confined to this habitat and could not escape the approaching anaerobic water. The same is the case with many bottom-living organisms. It is to be expected that only surface-dwellers will find suitable conditions in the open water of the future lake. Some others might survive between floating plants and material at the surface. We have already found several fish between the roots of the water-hyacinth, a plant which spreads rapidly after stagnation.

The surface area of the drowned forest is very large. The water between the dead trees is very quiet, and in the dry months of April and May an extensive growth of algal mats (*Spirogyra, Mougeotica*) was found. Also duckweed developed into dense mats. Here also organisms were found which did not occur in the former running water, but which were typical for stagnant water. These were the snails *Acroloxus, Gundlachia, Drepanotrema anatinum* and *Aplexa marmorata*. The crustaceans *Euryalona occidentalis, Chydorus*, nymphs of dragonflies, *Microvelia* and *Belostoma* were also found. In a rainy period the algal mats and duckweeds were destroyed. The dead leaves of trees were covered with muddy tubes of oligochaetes (*Dero, Aulophorus*). The oxygen content in the algal mats was very high, but at a short distance in the open water and in the depth it was soon absent. In the water of the former Sarakreek many iron bacteria were present. Soon after stagnation they formed a thick brown film on the water. The colour of the water changed from turbid-brown to dark. This was also the case at Afobaka. Chemical analyses of the water, made on a few occasions, showed an increase of phosphate, nitrate and organic matter. Under the anaerobic conditions in the layers below 3–4 m the amount of iron is high and the hydrogen sulphide present may produce iron sulphide. Together with the low pH and the carbon dioxide aggressivity of the water, these alterations may be of great importance for the management of the lake and the turbines.

The dead trees of the submerged forest will not decay in this acid anaerobic water, as may be deduced from observations elsewhere. At the water surface aerobic decomposition of the wood may cause the breakdown of the parts of the tree which remain above the water. The remaining submerged stumps will prevent water circulation, which will increase oxygen depletion. It is probable that after filling the lake the water flowing through it will follow the former river-bed. This will leave large parts completely stagnant. The trees will also prevent horizontal movements caused by wind action. The remaining trees also prevent fishing with nets. As large parts of the forest will remain above the water a swampy vegetation will develop around the tops, which will provide breeding places for mosquito larvae. Also snails will find favourable conditions, as is already recorded for several species. The vector of bilharzia (*Tropicorbis*) has not yet been found in the waters of Surinam farther inland, as the water is too acid. This is supported by the fact that also in the Amazon region no vectors of bilharzia were found by Sioli, except in one area where the soil contained lime. The environmental conditions in the future Brokopondo lake also may be considered unfavourable for snails.

As a habitat for snails, midge larvae and many other organisms the vigorous development of the water-hyacinth (*Eichhornia crassipes*) must be mentioned. The plant was very scarce in the former Suriname River and it is still scarce in the upper reaches of the river. In Surinam it is present in the coastal swamps and in some acid rivers. Soon after stagnation it multiplied rapidly in the lake. The botanist of our team, Dr. J. van Donselaar, plotted its distribution on maps. In the middle of 1965 large fields of water-hyacinth were found on both sides of the former river banks over a distance of about 70 km. The conditions of the lake environment were quite favourable for the water-hyacinth as the water became stagnant and the mineral content and the light intensity at the water surface increased when the trees lost their leaves. The Surinam Aluminum Company started a control programme. In the Sarakreek another plant developed, the water-fern *Ceratopteris thalictroides*. In May 1965 this plant covered an area of 1·5 km². The little water-fern *Salvinia* has not yet been recorded from the lake.

Data about the mammals and birds present in the lake region have been collected only incidentally. Many animals were rescued by the operation "Tjali oede Gwamba".

REFERENCES

Carter, G. S. (1934). Freshwaters of rainforest areas of British Guiana. *J. Linn. Soc.*, Zool. **39**(No. 264), 147–193.

Lindroth, A. (1957). Abiogenic gas supersaturation of river water. *Arch. Hydrobiol.* **53**(4), 589–597.

Mortimer, C. H. (1956). The oxygen content of air-saturated fresh waters and aids in calculating percentage saturations. *Proc. int. Soc. Limnol. Mitt.* **6**, 1–20.

Schulz, J. P. (1954). Vergelijkend Literatuuronderzoek inzake de ecologische consequenties van het "Combinatie-plan Surinamerivier". *Uitg. Natuurw. Stud-Kring. Suriname.*

Schmassmann, H. (1955). Die Stoffhaushalts-Typen der Fliessgewässer. *Arch. Hydrobiol.* Suppl. **22**(3/4), 504–509.

Sioli, H. (1964). General features of the limnology of Amazonia. *Proc. int. Soc. Limnol.* **15**(2), 1053–1058.

Utermöhl, H. (1958). Zur Gewässertypenfrage tropischer Seen. *Proc. int. Soc. Limnol.* **13**(1), 236–249.

Discussion

WORTHINGTON: Brokopondo provides an interesting contrast with Kariba and Volta. There are similarities in the chemical changes, but an important difference is that at Brokopondo the land flooded was mostly covered by closed canopy rain-forest, whereas these African lakes were in savanna woodland country. At Brokopondo there was no clearing at all, the forest trees are 50 m high and the water depth is to be 50 m. Were there sufficient areas of open water among the trees—along the river—to sample the open water for comparison with stations among the trees?

LEENTVAAR: We made ten sampling stations, some midstream in the Suriname River and some among the trees; details will be published elsewhere. There was no oxygen amongst the trees, from top to bottom; conditions in the open water spaces contrasted with those stations among the trees.

McCONNELL: You report that *Eichhornia* developed along the main river and *Ceratopteris* in Sara creek. Were there any chemical reasons for this? Also who moved the people?

LEENTVAAR: It is not known why *Eichhornia* developed in one place, and *Ceratopteris* in another. The Government moved the people.

Nile Control and its Effects on Insects of Medical Importance

D. J. LEWIS*

c/o British Museum (Natural History), London, England

The arid climate of Egypt and the northern Sudan creates a heavy demand for water in the low-Nile season, which has led to the development of several reservoirs and to alteration of the natural flow in the intervening reaches. Most of the control schemes are outlined in a short book by Newhouse (1939). In my former capacity as entomologist to the Ministry of Health of the Sudan Republic I studied insects of medical importance along the Nile from time to time, and observed some ways in which Nile control has affected the natural history of the river.

In the swampy Sudd region of the Upper Nile much water is lost by evaporation, and there is a plan to reduce this loss by making a by-pass canal. A Government team investigated the probable results of this plan which would doubtless affect cattle-grazing and the breeding areas of tabanid flies which attack cattle and may transmit cattle trypanosomiasis mechanically.

Downstream on the White Nile is the Jebel Auliya reservoir. In 1862 Sir Samuel Baker observed "floating water plants massed together and forming green swimming islands, sometimes slowly descending with the sluggish stream, bearing spectre-like storks thus voyaging on nature's rafts from lands unknown". These were papyrus and other plants from the Sudd, which drifted ashore and helped to form mosquito-breeding swamps. Such plants are among the many aquatic organisms of the Nile system which travel great distances, so that a full study of their biology would be a very complex process. The Jebel Auliya reservoir began to operate in 1937 and the slowing of the current caused the rafts to become stranded far upstream. Other plants flourished in an ecological succession, including the sedge *Cyperus rotundus* and also *Najas pectinata* which formed spongy masses suitable for the larvae of certain species of anopheline mosquitoes. After nine years the grasses *Echinochloa stagnina* and *Vossia cuspidata* (small form) had formed a vast raft in the Kosti area, which smothered the *Najas* and supported a sparse population of larvae of *Anopheles pharoensis*. This mosquito caused much

*Member of the Scientific Staff of the Medical Research Council.

annoyance but was not an important vector of malaria because it is exophilic and there was no vegetation to shelter it near houses. Plans were considered for drying the grass as fodder, but it was necessary to take precautions against the multiplication of *Najas* and against liver fluke which had affected cattle when the palatable sweet grasses had replaced the tough unattractive sedge. Some twenty years after the dam was completed *Eichhornia crassipes* arrived and again changed the ecological picture. The long period of ecological succession emphasizes the difficulty of forecasting the consequences of interfering with the Nile.

One early result of the constant water level during storage was the formation of small sand bars which enclosed pools suitable for larvae of the dangerous malaria vector *A. gambiae.*

The population to be protected against malaria was reduced by the removal of many people to alternative livelihood schemes in the Gezira irrigated area. This was one result of extensive surveys before the reservoir was established.

In this rather dry latitude there is another class of man-made lake, the small reservoir for storing rain water, which was generally far from any source of water plants.

On the Blue Nile, the Roseires Dam will doubtless affect many organisms including *Simulium damnosum* which transmits human onchocerciasis in some parts of the Sudan.

The daily discharge of this river in the rains may approach 1 000 million tonnes of water, carrying a heavy load of silt. In the Sennar reservoir, near the dam, *E. stagnina* grew on silt deposits and formed an extensive raft in more than 3·6 m of water when the level rose in November. It would be difficult to control mosquito larvae in this grass by adjusting water levels, even if several factors did not make this procedure impracticable. Little *E. stagnina* grew near the shore at Sennar, where the ground was rapidly flooded during the cool dry season. Some early attempts to diminish the grass raft were stopped because they caused some of the *A. pharoensis* to be replaced by *A. gambiae.*

The alluvial basins at the bends of the Blue Nile were originally overgrown with *sunt* trees, *Acacia arabica*, and the water regime of the Sennar reservoir has converted many of the basins into man-made lakes. In the southern ones prolonged flooding increased the breeding of *A. gambiae*, while in the north trees were drowned and grasses flourished and made conditions favourable for *A. pharoensis* and certain culicines.

S. damnosum bred in the spillways of the Sennar Dam.

In the Gezira cotton area, which is irrigated by water from Sennar, many of the canals are designed for storing water at night and thus form small reservoirs. A few Nile water plants and the Palaearctic *Potamogeton perfoliatus* colonized some canals and increased the need for precautions against *A. gambiae* and the snail vectors of schistosomiasis. Residual pools in the field channels presented a special problem in the control of this mosquito.

Along the Blue Nile between Sennar and Khartoum the extraction of irrigation water created lake-like conditions in the dry season, which favoured the multiplication of chironomid midges of the genus *Tanytarsus*. The larvae rose to the surface at night and drifted a long way downstream. Many of them reached Khartoum where the river is ponded by the unnaturally high water of the White Nile below the Jebel Auliya Dam. The adult midges caused intense annoyance and some people became allergic to them.

On parts of the main Nile between Khartoum and Dongola the *nimitti* fly, *Simulium griseicolle*, is a very serious pest of man and animals, and its incidence is doubtless affected by manipulation of the water level.

The Wadi Halfa area is influenced by the southern end of the reservoir formed by the Aswan Dam. *Tanytarsus* became such an important pest that at times an asthma camp was built in the desert and the removal of the town was considered. Wadi Halfa is near the boundary between the Ethiopian and Palaearctic zoogeographical regions and near the northern or southern limits of several species of insects. One of these is *A. gambiae*, and future changes in water level are liable to affect, for better or worse, the possibility that it may spread into the middle of Egypt as it did over twenty years ago. Near the frontier the water table, raised by the reservoir, caused the Faras basin to be flooded with salt water. The salt created an agricultural problem but fortunately favoured the harmless *A. multicolor* instead of *A. gambiae*.

Publications on these and some other insects of the Nile reservoirs may be located by reference to Lewis (1958). Much is known about the climate and hydrology of the Nile but its biology still offers an unlimited field for research.

REFERENCES

Lewis, D. J. (1958). *Trans. R. ent. Soc. Lond.* **110**, 81–98.
Newhouse, F. (1939). "The Training of the Upper Nile." Pitman, London.

General Discussion

WORTHINGTON: I would like to ask Dr. J. Rzoska and Dr. J. Talling about the hydrobiology of the longer-established Nile lakes.

RZOSKA: The Nile dams which we studied in the Sudan were Jebel Auliya, a 600 sq. km lake in savanna country completed in 1937, and the smaller (140 sq. km) Sennar dam lake completed in 1925. Work done on these two lakes by Dr. J. Talling, myself and others in the 1950s included physico-chemical aspects and the development of phyto- and zooplankton. Nothing has been done on the benthos. Both lakes gave the impression of stabilization of biological regimes. Jebel Auliya as part of the White Nile system has suffered a severe *Eichhornia* invasion, the limnological effects of which have not yet been fully assessed.

TALLING: Dr. Rzoska's comment regarding stabilization appears to be supported by observations made from Khartoum, between 1951 and 1956, on seasonal changes in physical and chemical water characteristics and phytoplankton populations. These features showed a very considerable degree of seasonal regularity, strongly influenced by the annual impoundment of water behind the Jebel Auliya and Sennar dams. However, these two reservoir systems differ from most examples discussed today in their complete annual release of stored water.

I would draw attention to the wide range of water chemistry encountered in the impounded African river waters. Among the major ions, the variation of bicarbonate plus carbonate concentration ("alkalinity") is perhaps particularly significant. The Nile is on the upper end of the scale, relatively alkaline, Jebel Auliya has a pH of 9·4, higher than most of the other African waters under discussion; in West Africa the pH is probably much less.

WORTHINGTON: Would Dr. White, who has just returned from Nigeria where he has been leading a team to study the effects of the Niger dam, tell us about these studies?

WHITE: Flooding above the dam at present being constructed across the River Niger at Kainji is due to start in 1967. Meanwhile studies on the hydrobiology and fisheries of the river before flooding have been organized by the University of Ife in co-operation with the University of Liverpool with funds from the United Kingdom Government. Of the team of fourteen scientists who have just spent the long vacation on this study, several are attending this meeting. Professor W. E. Kershaw who is working on *Simulium*, M. J. Holden, J. W. Banks and R. H. McConnell on fish, M. P. Thomas on zooplankton, J. W. Eaton on algae and myself on water chemistry, and we would like to discuss these aspects with others here who are interested, though our results are not yet worked out. Our botanist, C. D. K. Cook, is unfortunately not here, but he found many sudd-forming grasses and floating aquatics—potential trouble-makers.

HAMILTON: Can any speaker say how much notice is needed for biologists to be able to make useful prognostications for engineers?

BEAUCHAMP: The work being done now on existing projects will assist in anticipating future difficulties. Some useful information can also be derived from all the work that has been done on the natural lakes of Africa, though there is an important difference between these and the new man-made lakes. The new lakes are lakes filled with river water, whereas the old lakes are filled with lake water. The ancient lakes receive very little water from their inflows; they each have their own weather system and receive most of their water from rain falling directly on them, rain derived from water evaporated from them. This closed system means that water in these lakes has been worked on biologically for many years. Some of the chemical constituents in the water are utilized and precipitated as organic matter, and this organic matter on decomposition leads to the differential release of these constituents, with the result that the lake water develops a chemical composition quite different from that of the water flowing in. The total volume of the water contained in the new lakes could be supplied by the river in two or three years, but the natural lakes are quite different. The extreme example is Lake Tanganyika; if this lake were empty it would take 1 500 years for it to fill if the water received were that from its inflows.

GILSON: May I add that how long biological studies should be pursued in order to assess potential hazards is an important question which biologists are reluctant to face. Engineers and politicians are more concerned with orders of magnitude, whereas the biologist thinks too much in precise quantitative terms. Biologists cannot give precise answers, only look at what is already there, study analogous cases, and then make intelligent guesses; and engineers must be content with an answer that cannot be too definite, but can only list the probabilities. It is sometimes difficult to persuade engineers that large sums should be spent to cover something which may not happen. Also nature sometimes puts her own mistakes right and what seems a disaster may moderate later; for example, the water weed *Elodea canadensis* is no longer a problem in this country and *Salvinia* on Lake Kariba seems to be dying down. Therefore biologists need to think more in terms of orders of magnitude rather than precise terms when advising.

WORTHINGTON: This question is also of interest to medical and finance people. It generally requires several years to assess biological situations. Kariba now seems to have achieved a steady state and Jebel Auliya was evidently stable some fifteen years after impoundment.

YONGE: The unpredictability of the changes which may follow alteration from river to dam or from estuarine to freshwater conditions is very unlikely to be less in the establishment of the reservoir at Plover Cove in the New Territory, Hong Kong. Here an arm of the sea, some 3 miles long and about 1 mile wide, is being cut off by erection of dams across the narrow opening, already partly occupied by an island. The water, some 40 ft deep, will then be pumped out so that the basin will be ready to be filled with fresh water at the beginning of the rainy season. There is a substantial and high catchment area. It is certainly predictable that all organisms in the bottom mud will be killed as soon as any appreciable amount of fresh water enters. It is less easy to predict how long this amount of dead, largely animal, matter will take to decay. Obviously much will depend on vertical circulation; if necessary, measures will have to be taken to prevent stratification. It must be realized that the water is to be used for drinking and for domestic purposes generally. A biologist is at work studying the nature and especially the bulk—the biomass—of animal and plant life and making all necessary chemical and physical measurements in the water enclosed in the confines of the future reservoir. The possibility of invasion by floating vegetation is realized, also that the water may become a breeding ground for insects. Although some fish and freshwater invertebrates and some plants will enter from the existing streams, it may be necessary to augment these and so hasten as much as possible the establishment of a balanced freshwater community which will include edible fish.

DREW: What we have learned from previous papers highlights two rather different approaches or attitudes of mind. First, that of the engineer who imposes a discontinuity or "stop change" by the construction of a dam or barrage, i.e. a deliberate manifestation of major physical factors to attain certain ends. Second, that of the biologist, who in an almost detached way, seems largely to observe the often adverse "natural" sequence of water chemistry developments.

It is obviously very difficult to predict final ecological balances but encouraging to learn that stability may be reached in fifteen years, rather than in 1 500 years.

With the figure of several million pounds having been mentioned as incurred, e.g. in bush clearing to mitigate the consequences of oxygen depletion etc., would it not be worthwhile at least to consider more positively engineering intervention, e.g. oxygenation, pH adjustment etc., in order to establish conditions for biological viability and productivity, albeit at new levels and perhaps with, for example, different fish species?

FORD: There is a great need for engineers to have advance information from biologists on many aspects of man-made lakes. For example, it would be invaluable if biologists could predict phenomena such as the isolated high iron content of 3·1 p.p.m. in Kariba water (see Table I, p. 13) or the drop in pH from 6·5 to 5·5 at Brokopondo (p. 37).

EWER: In connexion with the question raised by Professor Yonge about the Hong Kong reservoir, there are certain obvious questions which one can ask. Will there be thermal stratification? In this respect Volta is very different from Kariba, but very similar to Brokopondo and it seems reasonable to expect that conditions at Kainji will be like those on Volta. Beauchamp is right in saying that we must go through a data-gathering stage, learning what it is that is important to know for prediction and what we can forget about for the time being. The engineers are often not forthcoming in saying what they want to know: the ability to formulate the questions well is of importance.

DOUGLAS: I would like to add to what Professor Ewer has just said. On Kariba had the engineers consulted the biologists they could have predicted certain things. The *Salvinia* outbreak could have been predicted (and this caused a panic in 1960–61, though it is not now the trouble that we thought that it was going to be); also with the flooded vegetation and high rate of decay, the deoxygenation could have been predicted (and this led to turbine trouble from the hydrogen sulphide and copper contacts were blackened). Some of these things can be predicted.

WORTHINGTON: Prediction is only possible on past experience, and ten years ago there was extremely little information available. Are biologists now happier to make predictions for the next man-made lakes?

EWER: Certainly we have learnt a lot. It is clear that strictly tropical low-lying lakes are different from high-altitude lakes or sub-tropical lakes like Kariba. Kariba is totally different from Volta and Brokopondo. But what will happen at Nasser seems to me an open question.

DE BONT: The way in which such lakes as Volta, Brokopondo, Kainji-Bussa, develop is certainly not the same as for lakes situated in savanna or desert regions. In order to have an idea of what is going on in lakes in forested country one should look at such waters as the Stanley-Pool on the River Congo. The conditions there are certainly sufficiently settled so as to give a good picture of what is likely to develop in man-made lakes in tropical forests.

Problems Arising from the Making of Man-made Lakes in the Tropics

The Establishment of Fisheries in Man-made Lakes in the Tropics

P. B. N. JACKSON

Food and Agriculture Organization of the United Nations, UNSF Fisheries Research Project, Lake Victoria, Jinja, Uganda

SUMMARY

Man-made lakes, being formed by barriers on rivers, are generally disadvantageous to anadromous or katodromous fish and their fisheries, but in most other cases, especially in the tropics, a large increase in the fish population can be expected. Those species which in the riverine regime preferred sluggish, stagnant water habitats show a relative increase in numbers, usually immense, over those which were current-loving in the previous regime. The new species composition is favourable to the establishment of a fishery, as the still-water fish are usually of considerable commercial value. After an initial period of extremely high fertility, with very rapid increase in numbers of aquatic organisms, comparatively high water fertility, relative to equivalent natural waters, is to be expected due to greater inflow and outflow in artificial impoundments. Other differences between natural and artificial waters include short-term phenomena, such as initial deoxygenation, and long-term effects, e.g. more considerable silting and a large annual draw-down. Management techniques include thorough pre-impoundment biological and physical surveys of the rivers and dam basins, pre-impoundment bush clearing and harbour construction. Many tropical African fishes use fishways with facility, dams often being restocked from below if barriers are negotiable. Stocking of tropical waters with foreign species must be carefully considered, but may be done to introduce a species hardy to adverse conditions, to colonize new niches to which none of the original fish are adapted, or to introduce new species similar but supposedly superior to the endemic. In large new lakes fishery training is usually necessary, and helpful where rehabilitation of people displaced from the lake basin is concerned; this needs careful planning and organization. A high, even if simple, standard of fishing and product processing and disposal must be inculcated from the start. Conservation legislation must be introduced *ab initio* but used sparingly after the large post-impoundment stocks are established. The importance of recreational fishing in man-made lakes, providing local recreation and tourist income, is stressed.

INTRODUCTION

As the number of large impoundments of flowing water on the earth's surface become rapidly more numerous, the importance of establishing fisheries in them increases yearly. A fishery, either commercial or recreational, or both, can readily be established in most of such impoundments, even in those of small size, and in most cases in the tropics can form a significant and most valuable additional source of protein food. This paper attempts a brief review of the subject in general, with particular reference to tropical impoundments; the subject, however, is so large that treatment must necessarily be cursory. While the word "lake" is in common usage for waters ranging from dams of a few acres in area to the huge schemes on the world's greatest rivers, emphasis here is to some extent placed on the large impoundments, although, since successful fisheries can be established in most of the many thousands of small water conservation or irrigation dams throughout the tropics, and the same species of sluggish-water fish thrive equally well in many smaller impoundments, the treatment is again largely general in regard to size of the man-made lake.

Since most man-made lakes of large size in the tropics are new, there is also, unavoidably, an emphasis on the changes which occur in the early stages, during the filling period which may take three or four to as much as ten years or more, and immediately after. An emphasis on change is, however, appropriate in all considerations of fresh waters at the present time, since a state of change is usual and a static state more and more rare in modern times. Whether the change is caused by man's ever-increasing impact on his environment, or, more rarely, caused by natural climatic changes such as those which have recently raised the level of the African great lakes, it is at present inevitable and a major factor in fishery management. The phrase "maximum sustained yield" remains ever the goal, but the yearly yield itself is ever changing through changes both in gross fish population and species composition. These may arise from natural causes, or the more common effects of man's activities, such as increasing human population pressure raising water fertility to, and past, the point where pollution occurs, by altering water run-off by over-grazing, burning, etc., by the accidental or deliberate introduction of exotic organisms, by over- or under-fishing or by controlling and impounding water.

No consideration of the establishment of fisheries in man-made lakes should therefore be undertaken without an appreciation of the ever-present factor of change, which though occurring in all waters, is of especial and particular application in artificial impoundments.

General Considerations

A man-made lake may be defined as a large body of standing water, usually fresh, which exists as a result of impoundment of water which would otherwise run away from a catchment area. Major reasons for construction of such impoundments nearly always are the providing of a head of water for the generation of hydro-electric power, or for the creation of a reservoir for irrigation, or, often, both. Sometimes the primary purpose is flood control. But the establishment of a fishery is almost always a secondary consideration.

A fishery by definition involves the capture of fish and other aquatic animals for the benefit of mankind; this benefit is either that of more food, here called a commercial fishery, or of its recreational value to people and its economic value in this regard in bringing money to an area or country; this we call a recreational fishery. Both recreational and commercial fisheries have at source the primary objective of catching fish; the benefit occurs when more, or more valuable in the economic or aesthetic sense, fish are caught after impoundment than before it.

Therefore, while the establishment of a fishery is only one, and very often a comparatively minor factor among those considered when planning a new impoundment, when this factor is considered it should be on the first premise of whether or not the lake will create a better state of affairs than that obtaining before impoundment, in regard to the fishery. Virtually every impoundment, in fact, has a fishery potential, but this may be either positive, in comparison with the situation before impoundment, or negative. Thus proper planning and costing of a new man-made lake, primarily intended for hydro-electric power or irrigation though it may be, should take account of the fishery potential in these terms. If the future potential is expected to be negative *vis-à-vis* the old situation, then the new lake must firstly be to this extent even more justifiable in terms of the economic benefit it is expected to bring, and secondly extensive research must be undertaken to minimize the adverse effects of the new project on the fishery. If the fishery potential is expected to be positive, this expectation can be used further to justify the project or to make increased expenditure on it. Regrettably often in the past, however, the factor of future fisheries has simply not been considered at all by those responsible for a new impoundment, or erroneously assumed to be a negligible consideration, or at best ignored in the hope that no harm would occur.

NEGATIVE FISHERY POTENTIALS

In a man-made lake a negative fishery potential is very largely caused by the project forming an obstruction to the migration of anadromous fishes, coupled in many instances with the adverse flooding of upstream spawning grounds for such fishes. While we are dealing primarily with tropical waters, the example may be given that in almost no case can the numerous dams constructed on the cold salmon rivers of Canada be regarded as anything but injurious to the fishery. Here the considerations mentioned above apply: dam construction must proceed in spite of, and in no sense because of, the fishery, and must therefore be considered even more justifiable for the economic development of the country than would otherwise be the case. Considerable additional expense in regard to the construction of fishways must often be incurred, and even then migrating fish have considerably more difficulty in their journeys (Brett, 1957). Management problems of and necessary research into the fishery becomes immensely more complex (Andrew and Geen, 1960) with a host of factors such as changes of temperature and water quality, design of fishways, artificial transportation of fish, artificial spawning and many others to be considered. It is frequently necessary, where the fishery represents a valuable resource, to conduct research into the physical features of the structure obstructing passage, such as design of dam wall, penstocks and turbines, etc. (Kramer and Oligher, 1964).

While an extensive literature has grown up in regard to efforts to reconcile important commercial fisheries of anadromous fish with hydro-electric development, there is less on those fish populations which are not or not yet commercially valuable or at present valuable only to a small number of people who use them for food or recreation. Yet there are man-made lakes which have quietly exterminated a population of fish in the river the lake was made on, and there will be more. This is because the economic worth of the fish was not considered sufficient to warrant the expense of constructing a fishway or, as Jackson (1963) has pointed out, because the dam or series of dams on the river impound more water than is permissible to maintain an adequate downstream flow. The numerous eels of the Tana River, Kenya (Frost, 1955), appear almost certainly doomed to extinction as a result of a large irrigation and hydro-electric project at present being developed. The scheme calls ultimately for the construction of four dams across the Tana, for electricity and irrigation, and when all are completed it seems probable that water will be stored, in this low-rainfall area, to the extent that there will no longer be any flow in the lower reaches of the river, thus preventing any further migration of eels to and from the sea.

Positive Fishery Potentials

The majority of man-made lakes, excluding the above considerations regarding anadromous or katadromous fish, should show an increase in the fish biomass and therefore a positive fishery potential. The species involved are those of the original population, nearly always living in a fluviatile environment, which benefit from the new stagnant and lacustrine conditions and find here a new and greatly enlarged environment. Many riverine species, the majority in most tropical waters, use sheltered and semi-stagnant areas of the rivers to spawn and reproduce themselves (Jackson, 1961). The creation of a dam enlarges and multiplies such favourable environments, providing in addition increased food supplies and cover from predators.

In such species this state of affairs results in an immediate removal of much of the pressures previously limiting the size of the population, there is a marked decline in the natural mortality particularly of young fishes, and the age structure of the population is at once rapidly changed due to the high survival rate of the young fish spawned after inundation (Jackson, 1960a). Within a comparatively short space of time a fresh population equilibrium, at a higher level than the old, is reached. Patriarche (1957) estimated that the carrying capacity of Clearwater Lake, Missouri, was reached five years after inundation.

This pattern of an increased population is generally to be expected after impoundment. The species involved are generally those whose natural habitats include ponds and small lakes, and are very often cyprinids, siluroids, centrarchids and cichlids. Thus Ganapati and Chacko (1951) found the baril (*Barilius gatensis*) to have bred and multiplied prolifically in the old-established Kodaikanal Lake, India, first impounded in 1860. The Vaal River, South Africa, fished by anglers ever since its impoundment in 1938, has as its mainstay four species only, the ubiquitous carp (*C. carpio*), two other cyprinids, *Barbus holubi* and *Labeo capensis*, and the siluroid *Clarias gariepinus* (Du Plessis and Le Roux, 1965). The sluggish-water cyprinid *Tinca tinca*, the tench, flourishes in many European and Australian impoundments (Weatherly, 1958). In North America the family Centrarchidae, freshwater basses, sunfishes, crappies, etc., are exceptionally well represented in artificial impoundments. Certain genera such as *Lepomis*, *Micropterus* and *Pomoxis*, though originally restricted to individual natural waters in various parts of the U.S.A., have now been so transplanted as to be found in virtually every state of the Union. In tropical African waters fishes of the family Cichlidae, and particularly of the genus *Tilapia*, are usually the most important. Few impoundments here fail to have *Tilapia* as the most desired component of the commercial fishery catches (Maar, 1958; Mortimer, 1961; Bailey, 1965).

Nearly all of these fishes have in common the fact that they live and reproduce almost as well in ponds and small bodies of water as in large lakes; many in fact are in general called pond fishes. This is the key to the successful establishment of fisheries in man-made lakes; since the species at present forming the greatest component of catches, especially in tropical waters, are inhabitants of relatively shallow, well vegetated areas, the aim should firstly be to ensure that such conditions, in effect a continuous reduplication of pond-like environments, occur around the perimeter of the lake. The more such conditions occur, the greater will be the production of such fishes, the mainstay of fisheries in man-made lakes. Such fishes will increase in numbers in the new impoundment relative to those which prefer sluggish water less (Harding, 1964). In Kariba, as well, species previously known only from weedy upland streams in the area, and not from the Zambezi itself before impoundment, are now to be found. *Alestes imberi* and *Haplochromis philander*, for example, are now modestly common in the impoundment though previously not recorded from the river (L. B. Joeris, personal communication).

Draw-down and other Differences between Man-made and Natural Waters

Establishment of fisheries in man-made lakes depends largely upon how such waters differ from natural lakes and the effect such differences have on the fisheries. These differences include primary effects found soon after impoundment, such as initial deoxygenation of water, high primary fertility, etc., and the long-term effects that the fishery will have to live with, such as draw-down and the effects of silting.

A man-made lake impounds a large body of water over an extensive land area which has not previously been flooded and in the tropics usually bears a large cover of terrestrial vegetation. Extensive deoxygenation of the flooding lake soon after closure of the barrier may occur while the infant lake is still comparatively shallow and much rotting of land vegetation killed by the rising water occurs. Such a phenomenon occurred, for example, in the very early stages after closure of the Volta dam (Beauchamp, 1964, in litt.). Such deoxygenation may result in an extensive kill of the original riverine fish population, but these kills are rarely complete, if only for the reason that deoxygenation is always much lessened in the upper reaches of the young impoundment, where river water is flowing in. Thus, while the original riverine population may be severely reduced in numbers, it is seldom exterminated by initial deoxygenation, and the effect is generally soon nullified by the rapid post-impoundment population explosion. This phase is usually of short duration; as filling proceeds wave action over the increasing water area oxygenates the upper layers, and secondly wherever the new standing water gains some depth a thermocline is very rapidly established, as happened in the case of Kariba (Harding, 1961), so the epilimnion, covering the all-important shallow marginal area, is oxygenated.

The hypolimnion in man-made lakes may, at first, be more severely reduced than is the case in natural waters, due to the decay of the land vegetation killed by the rising waters. This may again, however, be only a temporary phenomenon, wearing off after a few years when decomposition of this vegetation is complete to the extent that only trunks and branches of the larger trees remain. Very rapid changes can often be observed in this regard in the early years of an impoundment's life. In Kariba, for example, reduction of bottom waters appears to be very much less in 1965 than 1964, and divers have very recently observed fish living below the thermocline at depths where they have not previously been recorded (Joeris, personal communication).

The phenomenon of high initial fertility, caused by nutrients leaching from a hitherto unflooded substrate is often spectacular in the early stages of impoundment. It is characterized by extensive plankton blooms (Stephens, 1949; Brook and Rzoska, 1954) followed by rapid establishment of aquatic vegetation and, consequent upon this, high reproduction and fast growth of other aquatic organisms including fish (Balinsky and James, 1960). A decline from this very high initial level soon follows, however, caused partly by diminution of bottom leaching as the volume of water impounded increases and partly as the nutrients are taken up by the aquatic vegetation as this becomes established and greater in quantity. After this stage has been passed, fertility, while at a lower level than the exceptionally high initial stages, may well remain higher than would be the case in comparable natural waters, since inflowing rivers usually bring a greater volume of water, and with it nutrients, into man-made than into natural lakes unless the latter are of relatively small size. Thus even the largest man-made impoundments will fill with water after a few years only, while the largest natural lakes, such as those of the African Rift Valleys would, if empty, take hundreds or even thousands of years to fill (Beauchamp, 1964).

For the establishment of a fishery, the ideal man-made lake might best have its waters conserved as much as possible all the year round, so as to preserve at all times the maximum height of water. In most dams however, being primarily built for electricity or irrigation, the reservoirs of water are tapped particularly during the dry seasons when the inflow from

c*

the river does not equal the outflow being used for these purposes. The result is a sinking of the water level, and this is usually periodic, happening at the driest time of the year. This annual sinking is known as the draw-down, and has a deleterious effect on the fisheries of many impoundments, particularly where these, in the tropics, are situated in dry, low-rainfall areas.

The main disadvantage of the draw-down is that it inhibits the permanent growth of aquatic vegetation in the important marginal areas of the dam. In many dams the annual draw-down is as much as 40 ft or even more, and the large marginal areas thus laid bare can carry only a flora of quick-growing plants, particularly algae, or of strongly-rooted vegetation that can stand desiccation, such as reeds (*Phragmites*). Many natural lakes, of course, experience a gradual seasonal draw-down caused by dry-season evaporation and outflow at a time when inflow is low. The difference in man-made lakes is, however, that the fall in water level is very often both much greater and very much more rapid where, for example, a large crop has to be irrigated at the hottest, driest time of the year when inflow is least and evaporation severest. Where the draw-down is rapid it may also expose areas being used for spawning, killing eggs and fry. This may be especially important in tropical African waters where the nest-building *Tilapia* are the most important commercial fish.

Where a severe annual draw-down is an inescapable fact of life so far as the fishery of a particular man-made lake is concerned, consideration as mentioned below must be given to the establishment of hardy fish and if possible to the establishment of pelagic species and artificial hatching facilities.

However, draw-downs are not always injurious, and deliberate drawdown is sometimes used as a management technique. This may be done, for example, to reduce stocks of undesirable fish, such as carp, in an impoundment by drastically reducing water volume, thus exposing and destroying eggs and facilitating removal of large quantities of the unwanted fish at the same time. Again, draw-down may be used to destroy weeds or thin out over-abundant vegetation.

Silting is another problem which in many cases can compromise the successful establishment of fisheries in man-made lakes. The effects of silt are nearly all adverse; heavy deposits will smother vegetation and inhibit its growth, choke and smother eggs on spawning areas, prevent the construction of nests on hard substrates, fill up reservoir areas and in general go far towards ruining the most productive fisheries in all but the very largest lakes.

Heavy silting is nearly always caused by soil erosion, itself a consequence of mismanagement of the land due to bad agricultural practices.

It is therefore to be avoided at all costs; besides being ruinous to fish in and out of man-made lakes (Jackson, 1963), other consequences of over-grazing and similar land management malpractices need no stressing here. It is desirable that a good deal of the perimeter of man-made lakes and where possible the immediate upper reaches of inflowing rivers should be preserved in the form of National Parks or nature reserves. Where this is not possible strict conservation farming according to the best usages should be practised. Where recreational fishing and the tourist industry are important economic factors, as they usually are or will be in the larger lakes, the establishment of nature preserves cannot help but contribute materially to such industries. The grazing of domestic livestock such as cattle, unless carefully controlled, can be extremely injurious, especially where overgrazing destroys emergent aquatic vegetation during low-water periods, thus preventing its use at high water for food production and cover for recently spawned fish. Fixed stock watering points should therefore be established where necessary and promiscuous access of livestock to the perimeter of the lake other-wise prevented or carefully controlled.

Where overgrazing and soil erosion are not a problem, the normal silt loads carried by a river may be beneficial to a very large impoundment built in a very rocky area of the river's valley. Such silt loads would be light in a large impoundment, and by settling on an otherwise stony and unproductive substrate, improve the productivity of an otherwise infertile area.

BUSH CLEARING, STOCKING AND OTHER MANAGEMENT PRACTICES

Establishment of fisheries in man-made lakes has as its aim the pro-duction of as much fish, of the most desirable species, as possible, the maximum yield that can be sustained year after year by commercial or recreational fishing without damage by over-fishing. Towards this end of achieving the maximum sustained yield various manipulations of the terrain and of the fish populations are possible. Such work should be started well before the actual construction and closure of the barrier impounding the lake.

Essential preliminary work includes a thorough knowledge of the fish population to be impounded. If this has not already been done a com-prehensive hydrobiological survey of the river regime should be initiated (Daget, 1961). This will identify and list the fish species present, the rela-tive abundance, ecological requirements and probable importance to the future fishery of each. A good knowledge, at least for the probably important species, should be obtained of their feeding habits, life histories, reproduction rates and age when spawning size is reached. At the same time all possible information should be amassed on the hydrology of the water, its seasonal flow, temperature and quality, the climate of the area, its size, vegetal cover, physical nature of the terrain and chemical nature of the various substrates in future to be covered.

Armed with these facts, or as many as possible, management can proceed with pre-impoundment planning. One early consideration is whether a migrant element is present and if so, the desirability of constructing a fishway and its type and design. Many fishways have been built, often at great expense, which have later proved to be failures for various reasons; either the design was wrong, or it was built in the wrong place or an adverse current was created so that fish failed either to find or be guided to it, or fish were unable or apparently did not wish to make use of it. These failures have led many to consider that fishways are not worth the expense of construction except where exceptionally valuable commercial fish such as salmon are concerned. On the other hand, there is considerable evidence that many species of African tropical fish will readily ascend fish ladders and enter impoundments above, as found for example by Daget (1950) at Markkala on the Middle Niger, and by Bell-Cross (1960) at Mwekera in Zambia. Observations by several authors on eels (*Anguilla* spp.) indicate that these fish will search for and find even the most difficult methods of circumventing a barrier, unless this is, like a giant dam wall, completely insurmountable. Hickling (1961) concludes from these and other findings that a dam will tend to be self-stocking from the stream below if the spillway is passable by the fish, and that their ascent is stimulated by an increased downflow of water.

Whether or not a fishway is to be constructed must be a matter for consideration on its merits in each case. Bearing in mind, however, that the capital cost of the fishway is, in the case of large man-made lakes, usually small in comparison with the cost of the scheme itself, and readily amortizable over the long length of time that the scheme is expected to exist, fishways should preferably be built where possible. At Kariba for example, where a ladder was not built, a number of large eels has recently been caught in the impoundment, but these are from the stock that was trapped in the river by the barrier and which will eventually die out, while many thousands of young elvers which at present congregate below the wall have no means of entry (Joeris, personal communication).

Another early consideration is the clearing of the bush and other dense vegetation commonly found in tropical impoundment basins, which is essential for the operation of nets in the future fishery. Unfortunately the capital cost of doing this is enormous in large tropical schemes, but again, by reason of the expected long length of life of the dam, as much should be spent on this as possible. Where a complete clearance is not possible for financial reasons, priority should be given to the clearing of the upper reaches which will form the shallow marginal areas of the new project. In Kariba, where complete clearance was not possible over this vast area, it was recommended (Jackson, 1961) that the first 60 ft down from maximum retention level be cleared. In addition priority in clearing should be given to sites where for one reason or another an especially productive fishery can be expected, such as around the mouth of an inflowing river shown by preliminary surveys to be especially high in dissolved nutrients.

Other work on the terrain before impoundment includes the construction of harbours, an easier and cheaper task before than after the site is covered with water, the deepening or creation of new channels to provide future water access to productive swamps, etc., according to the needs of each particular scheme. Consultation with the scheme's designers and engineers is desirable at all times, for example to explore possibilities towards reconciling some of the incompatibilities which might exist between hydro-electric and fishery needs. Thus engineers may demand the maximum head of water while the fishery manager might prefer the outflow at the bottom of the dam to get rid of as much of the deoxygenated reduced water below the thermocline as possible. But the fishery manager, if he succeeds in persuading the engineers to construct at least the sluice-gates for surplus water at a low level, must beware of flooding the downstream river with reduced water and destroying the life herein. Future gains must be balanced against future losses in all such considerations as these, and the importance of adequate hydrological study, particularly with reference to the thermocline, has recently been stressed by Allanson (1965).

Another extremely complex question is that of introducing new species of fish to supplement, or perhaps even partly to replace, the existing species in the impoundment. This is done for three reasons: firstly to introduce a hardy species which can cope with adverse conditions such as a severe annual draw-down or a very muddy, turbid water state; secondly to colonize new ecological niches to which none of the existing species are adapted, and thirdly to introduce a species of similar habits to the endemic but which is for various reasons considered to be more desirable in the fishery. The whole question of introducing organisms to environments foreign to them and where they may have no natural enemies or parasites, is delicate and fraught with danger; it is, so far as freshwater fish are concerned, discussed in principle by Myers (1955), the FAO Fisheries Biology Branch (1955) and Jackson (1960b). With this mention we leave the general principle and discuss the three cases mentioned above on the assumption that a decision attaching due weight to all factors will in each and every projected stocking be reached.

The species most used to stock muddy waters or impoundments barren of vegetation is the carp (*Cyprinus carpio*). While originally a temperate species the carp, because of its adaptability and hardiness, has been successfully stocked in many waters within the tropics where temperatures are not too high, such as in upland lakes (Maar, 1960), and selective breeding may produce varieties adapted to greater heat. Successful management techniques include the necessity for heavy fishing to avoid overproduction of this fecund fish, with a consequent overpopulation of small stunted individuals, spoiling and destroying the bottom substrate. The bulk of opinion is, however, against the introduction of carp into a new environment, and this fact should be borne in mind when stocking with this species is contemplated. Some cyprinids of the genus *Labeo* may also do well in adverse conditions, being grazers of sessile bottom algae, but most undertake an up-river migration for spawning in their native habitats, and stocking may fail for this reason. Certain of the algal-eating *Tilapia*, also, may thrive in the absence of higher vegetation if other conditions are suitable, and in many impoundments these may be the most suitable species to stock. In general, however, little is known of suitable fish for the many dams where a severe annual draw-down is inevitable, and there is need for much further research in this field.

Though not yet attempted on a large scale, one interesting management possibility for dams with a severe seasonal draw-down of a few months' duration, but which otherwise retain a good level of water, is to breed fingerlings of *Tilapia* or other suitable species in ponds adjacent to the impoundment, during the adverse period, and release them in large quantities as soon as the level increases. In these tropical waters, with abundant algal food and, equally important (van Someren and Whitehead, 1961), abundant living space, rapid growth to a relatively large size should ensue before harvesting is necessary.

The second reason for stocking is that of the utilization of vacant ecological niches. In most large man-made lakes where an originally riverine fish population is present, large areas of open water exist in which none of the local species are adapted for living. Consideration is often therefore given to introducing one of the several open-water or "pelagic" tropical freshwater fish. These in Africa include a number of species of freshwater sardine (family Clupeidae), notably two comparatively large species *Stolothrissa tanganicae* and *Limnothrissa miodon* from Lake Tanganyika, and a variety of species of the cyprinid genus *Engraulicypris*, distributed over a number of African Great Lakes and rivers.

There appears in general to be little reason why such fish should not be stocked, but as they are always fragile, with easily shed scales, physical difficulties of transportation are great. However, successful though of necessity elaborate techniques have been evolved (Capart, 1959; Collart, 1960) with the result that the safe introduction of such species is now practicable. Their establishment in the new environment is, however, another matter, but preliminary experiments in Kariba indicate that both *Stolothrissa* and *Limnothrissa* will survive for long periods in this lake.

Thirdly, fish are introduced because it is hoped that their desirable qualities will enable them to make the fishery more attractive than would be the case with local species only. In temperate waters there is a long history of salmonids and centrarchids being tried for this purpose, with varying but often little success. The failure of the Atlantic salmon (*Salmo salar*) to become established in Ontario despite hundreds of introductions is a case in point (Dymond, 1955). In tropical waters fish which are commonly thought by managers to possess superior qualities of growth, adaptability and food preferences are the carp, the Mozambique tilapia *T. mossambica* and the Chinese grass carp *Ctenopharyngodon idella*. Each, however, possesses drawbacks as well as advantages, of stunting, or undue destruction of local fish or habitat (Myers, 1955; CSA/CCTA, 1960), or of difficult establishment in tropical waters (Hickling, 1960; Slack, 1962) and so on. Again pros and cons must be most carefully weighed before introductions are attempted.

FISHING TECHNIQUES, CONSERVATION MEASURES AND TRAINING OF FISHERMEN

This large aspect of fishery establishment can here be mentioned only briefly, and with particular regard to the special problems in this field that arise in tropical man-made lakes.

In large impoundments the main primary consideration is that, due to the very large volume of water now present, much more extensive fishery opportunities exist than was the case in the old riverine regime. In some cases the previous inhabitants of the area were not fishermen at all, while in others the number of fishermen the old river could gainfully support is inadequate for the fishery needs of the new lake. Thus in almost every case an element of training, often large and extensive, is involved, and planning for it must commence at an early stage. More often than not people have to be removed from the lake basin before flooding begins, and training and otherwise assisting these to be fishermen is usually a useful factor in the rehabilitation problems that arise from their displacement.

A related social aspect of the new asset which is coming into being is that of whether there is a need to employ as many people in fishing as possible, or whether it is required that the removal of as many fish as economically as possible be the more important consideration due to adequate alternative local employment, etc. In the first instance large numbers of small fishermen with simple gear and craft will be encouraged while in the other a few large firms or organizations with a greater degree of capital investment, with more elaborate and expensive gear and vessels, but with less manpower involved, will be in the field. The main principles followed are firstly, that however simple the gear, it should be of good quality, i.e. gill nets of artificial fibre of the right thread and mesh-size, seaworthy and durable planked boats, reliable outboard motors with good maintenance facilities, etc. Similarly attention should be paid to ensuring that the product is of as high a quality as possible. This can and should be attained in even the simplest fishery by the provision of an adequate number of collection points where fish can readily be sold by the fishermen, ice and freezing facilities near enough at hand to ensure that wet fish is sold in as fresh a state as possible, adequate access roads and other communications and training in drying, salting and smoking techniques, where these are practised by the fishermen themselves before sale. Secondly, where concessions are granted to large firms and organizations, it must be remembered that monopolistic practices are as undesirable in the fishing industry as in any other, and their creation and establishment guarded against.

Where conservation measures are necessary, it is always easier to remove legal restrictions on fishing than to impose them. In principle, therefore, it is sounder practice when starting the brand-new fishery of a newly impounded lake to commence with conservation measures in force and remove or lighten them as experience shows, but with the precedent of their once having been there remaining in case of future need, than to attempt to impose them afterwards when custom, usage and vested interest have grown up in the fishery. Imposition may then be resented whatever the need and be in general more difficult. Another advantage of early imposition of the usual conservation measures is that, even though experience may prove not all of them to be strictly necessary, the first year or two after closure, when comparatively few adults of the old river population have to be the parents of an enormously increased lake-bred population, is a crucial period for the rapid build-up of stocks. Heavy fishing of the old river population in the first stages of the dam should therefore be discouraged, and conservation measures help to do this, until the much more numerous lake-bred progeny are old enough to be fished.

In general, conservation measures in force should be kept under constant review, and removed always as soon as possible. The fecundity of tropical fish stocks, and their ability to withstand heavy fishing, is extremely high, and in a well-managed fishery few if any conservation regulations, apart from the seasonal protection of spawning areas, prohibition of the use of explosives, etc., should prove to be necessary. The required legislation should, however, always exist, enabling individual measures to be quickly imposed as and when necessary.

RECREATIONAL FISHING

While the above has been discussed primarily with the establishment of a commercial fishery in mind, most applies equally well to the establishment of a successful and prosperous recreational fishery. The importance of man-made lakes in this regard should never be under-estimated, since pressure on recreational areas becomes ever more intense as human populations increase so rapidly in numbers and in amount of leisure time available. Thus in 1960 90% of all Americans took part in out-door recreation in some form, doing this on 4·4 billion occasions, but in the year 2000, the participation will increase to 12·4 billion occasions, an increase of 184%. By this time the population will have doubled, but participation in outdoor recreation will have trebled (Outdoor Recreation Resources Review Commission, 1962). Examples of the sport angling pressures per annum which can be expected are that the Tennessee Valley Authority reservoirs yield 36 lb of fish per acre per annum, as against an estimated 40–50 lb for the tropical Lake Kariba (Maar, 1959; Hickling, 1961), of which 27 lb go to anglers and 9 lb to commercial fishermen (Stroud, 1954), while in the Transvaal Province, South Africa, £3 000 000 per annum is spent by anglers alone (Opperman, 1965).

These examples emphasize the importance that should be placed on the establishment and development of recreational fishing in the public interest of the country, both as a very necessary recreational outlet, essential to the health and well-being of the people, and as a lucrative source of revenue from anglers and tourists. There is therefore every justification for the establishment of fish species for their angling value alone, even where their commercial significance might be expected to be secondary. Normal fish management practices apply here; for example, game species are very often predators upon other fish, and if the introduction of one is contemplated, the presence of an adequate population of forage fish must be assured. A case in point is the introduction of the Lake Tanganyika Nile perch into Kariba, which has been proposed but its consideration deferred until such time as a population of the pelagic clupeids (see above) from the same lake and on which the Nile perch largely feeds has been established.

ACKNOWLEDGEMENT

The advice and assistance given to me in the preparation of this paper by my colleague Mr. L. B. Joeris of the Food and Agriculture Organization, Project Manager of the Lake Kariba Fisheries Research Institute, who has freely made available his extensive experience of man-made impoundments, is gratefully acknowledged.

REFERENCES

Allanson, B. R. (1965). The significance of the thermocline in the biology of developing reservoirs. *S. Afr. J. Sci.* **61** (3), 132.

Andrew, F. J. and Geen, G. H. (1960). Sockeye and pink salmon production in relation to proposed dams in the Fraser River system. *Bull. int. Pacif. Salm. Fish. Comm., XI.*

Bailey, R. G. (1965). The dam fisheries of Tanzania. E. Afr. Soc. Biol. Res. Symposium, Kampala, Uganda, March 1965.

Balinsky, B. I. and James, G. V. (1960). Explosive reproduction of organisms in the Kariba Lake. *S. Afr. J. Sci.* **56**, 4.

Beauchamp, R. S. A. (1964). The Rift Valley Lakes of Africa. *Verh. Verein. theor. argew. Limnol.* **15**, 91.

Bell-Cross, G. (1960). Observations on the movement of fish in a fish-ladder in Northern Rhodesia. *In* "CSA/CTA Third Symposium on Hydrobiology and Inland Fisheries". Lusaka.

Brett, J. R. (1957). Salmon research and hydroelectric power development. *Bull. Fish. Res. Bd. Can.,* 114.

Brook, A. J. and Rzoska, J. (1954). The influence of the Gebel Aulyia Dam on the development of Nile plankton. *J. Anim. Ecol.* **23**, 101.

Capart, A. (1959). A propos de l'introduction du Ndakala (*Stolothrissa tanganicae*) dans le lac Kivu. *Bull. agric. Congo belge* **1** (4), 1083.

Collart, A. (1960). L'introduction du *Stolothrissa tangankiae* (Ndagala) au Lac Kivu. *In* "CSA/CCTA Third Symposium on Hydrobiology and Inland Fisheries." Lusaka.

CSA/CCTA (1960). "Third Symposium on Hydrobiology and Inland Fisheries." Discussions, p. 28. Publ. no. 63. Lusaka.

Daget, J. (1950). La passe à poissons de Markkala. *Bull. Inst. Afr. noire* **12**, (4).

Daget, J. (1961). Report on the Kainji Dam Project (Fisheries). *In* "CSA/CCTA Fourth Symposium on Hydrobiology and Inland Fisheries." Fort Lamy.

Du Plessis, S. S. and Le Roux, P. J. (1965). Sport fisheries in river development with reference to the Orange River scheme. *S. Afr. J. Sci.* **61** (3), 137.

Dymond, J. (1955). The introduction of foreign fishes in Canada. *Proc. int. Ass. theor. appl. Limnol.* **12**, 543.

FAO Fisheries Division Biology Branch. (1955). The problem of the introduction of foreign species into inland waters—both natural and cultivated species. *Fish Pap. FAO.* **2**, March 1955.

Frost, W. E. (1955). Observations on the biology of eels (*Anguilla* spp.) of Kenya Colony, East Africa. *Fishery Publs. colon. Off.* **6**, 1954.

Ganapati, S. V. and Chacko, P. I. (1951). A hydrobiological survey of the waters of the upper Palnis with a view to fish culture. *Arch. Hydrobiol.* **45**, 543.

Harding, D. (1961). Limnological trends in Lake Kariba. *Nature, Lond.* **191**, 119.

Harding, D. (1964). Hydrology and fisheries in Lake Kariba. *Verh. int. Verein. theor. argew. Limnol.* **15**, 139.

Hickling, G. F. (1960). Observations on the growth of the Chinese grass-carp, *Ctenopharyngodon idellus* C. V. *Malay. agric. J.* **43** (1), 49.

Hickling, C. F. (1961). "Tropical Fish Culture." Longmans, London.

Jackson, P. B. N. (1960a). Ecological effects of flooding by the Kariba Dam on Middle Zambezi fishes. *Proc. 1st. Fed., Sci. Congress, Salisbury, S. Rhodesia.*

Jackson, P. B. N. (1960b). On the desirability or otherwise of introducing fishes to waters that are foreign to them. *In* "CSA/CCTA Third Symposium on Hydrobiology and Inland Fisheries". Lusaka.

Jackson, P. B. N. (1961). "Kariba Studies: Ichthyology, the Fish of the Middle Zambezi." Manchester University Press.

Jackson, P. B. N. (1963). The impact of man on the tropical environment: water control and impoundments, the aquatic side. *Int. Un. Conserv. Nat. nat. Resour.* 9th Tech. Meeting.

Kramer, F. K. and Oligher, R. G. (1964). Passing fish through hydraulic turbines. *Trans. Am. Fish. Soc.* **93** (3), 243.

Maar, A. (1958). Dams and drowned-out stream fisheries in Southern Rhodesia. *Int. Un. Conserv. Nat. nat. Resour.* 7th Tech. Meeting.

Maar, A. (1959). The fish potential of Lake Kariba. *Proc. 1st Fish. Day S. Rhod.* p. 50. Govt. Printer, Salisbury.

Maar, A. (1960). Carp culture in Africa south of the Sahara. *In* "CSA/CCTA Third Symposium on Hydrobiology and Inland Fisheries". Lusaka.

Mortimer, M. A. E. (1961). A report on the conservation dam fisheries of Northern Rhodesia, 1951–1961. *J.F.R.O. A. Rep.* **11**. Govt. Printer, Lusaka.

Myers, G. S. (1955). Notes on the freshwater fish fauna of middle Central America, with especial reference to pond culture of *Tilapia. Fish. Pap. FAO.* **2**.

Opperman, R. W. J. (1965). The recreational potential of the Orange River Project. *S. Afr. J. Sci.* **61** (3), 147.

Outdoor Recreation Resources Review Commission (1962). "Outdoor Recreation for America." Washington, D.C.

Patriarche, M. H. (1957). The development of the fish population in a new flood-control reservoir in Missouri, 1948 to 1954. *Trans. Am. Fish. Soc.* **87**, 240.

Slack, H. D. (1962). The maturation of Chinese grass-carp (*Ctenopharyngodon idellus*) C. & V. in tropical waters. *Malay. agric. J.* **43** (4), 299.

Someren, V. D. van and Whitehead, P. J. P. (1961). The culture of *Tilapia nigra* (Gunther) in ponds. 5—The effect of progressive alterations, in stocking density on the growth of male *T. nigra. E. Afr. agric. For. J.* **26** (3), 145.

Stephens, E. (1949). *Microcystis toxica* sp. nov. A poisonous alga from the Transvaal and Orange Free State. *Trans. R. Soc. S. Afr.* **32**, 105.

Stroud, R. H. (1954). TVA fishing. *SFI Bull.* **148**, 2.

Weatherley, A. H. (1958). Tasmanian farm dams in relation to fish culture. *CSIRO. Aust. Div. Fish. Oceanog. Tech. Pap.* 4.

Discussion

P. B. N. JACKSON: I would like to ask Mr. L. S. Joeris, Project Manager of the FAO Lake Kariba Fisheries Research Institute, to bring us up to date on recent developments on Kariba.

JOERIS: The Institute was set up in January 1964. I arrived in July 1964 and other members of the staff in January 1965. The staff comprises four biologists, two economists, and one fish processing officer, together with supporting personnel including twenty-four Africans on data collection. We have good new equipment.

The fish breeding seasons that normally were revealed throughout the Zambezi River in the Kariba Lake area prior to the construction of the lake have changed drastically. Previously, breeding by most species occurred with the rise in water level brought on by the rainy season floods. With the establishment of the lake, spawning activity started with the slight rise in water temperature during late August or early September, and in several species takes place throughout the warmer months.

Important environmental changes occurring during recent years were most obvious during 1964 and 1965. Previous to this period the lake remained stratified for most of the year and oxygen depletion under the thermocline was complete throughout most of the period of stratification. During 1964 oxygen remained under the thermocline for most of the year and only occasionally was hydrogen sulphide encountered. During 1965 the lake remained oxygenated below the thermocline throughout the year over large areas and only an occasional trace of hydrogen sulphide was detected.

The presence of oxygen below the thermocline allowed fish to inhabit this area, and during periods of high surface temperature there was an almost complete absence of commercially important species in the cleared fishing areas where clearing had been carried out to a depth of approximately 60 ft.

During this same period aqualung divers observed large concentrations of *Labeo*, *Tilapia* and other desirable species starting at about 90 ft below the surface. Experimental nets set in areas sufficiently clear of trees to allow them to reach bottom, and nets fished just above tree tops by using a few buoys attached to the nets by long leads, produced good catches of most commercially important species. *Labeo* did demonstrate a preference for deeper water than the *Tilapia*, but both species were taken down to 160 ft in the deepest sets made. With the acquisition of new floats we shall be able to set satisfactory fish nets much deeper this year so as to determine the maximum depths utilized by various species throughout the year.

The year-round occurrence of oxygen below the thermocline should have a marked increase on the quality of bottom organisms produced in the lake as bottom deposits of silt and organic matter accumulate. Snail populations are developing rapidly in many of the *Salvinia* mats. They are being moved about the lake in these floating weed mats that have broken off from the prominent mat in river estuaries. Fish stomach analyses in recent months have revealed that these snails are becoming an extremely important food item in the diets of several species.

Much of the decline in production in 1964 must be attributed to the dispersal of fish into the deeper areas that were inaccessible to African fishermen with their present gear.

The floating weed mats that drift about the lake at certain seasons are proving to be excellent fishing sites; nets are fished 3–4 ft below the surface of the mats and little or no net damage is encountered.

Numerous other physical and biological changes are taking place, but they are much more gradual. These must be examined closely to determine the pattern that can be expected to occur in many of the larger lakes under construction in the tropics at the present time.

A fish processing plant which buys fish from the Africans for experimental processing was started in February. It uses all species of fish and has helped to induce changes in fishing and fish-eating habits around the lake.

WHITE: Has the chemical regime picture presented by Harding (p. 9) continued?

JOERIS: There has been little or no change.

HOLDEN: I should like to challenge Jackson's statement about the ability of tropical fish to withstand heavy fishing. In my experience this is not true. In Lake Victoria *Tilapia esculenta* have been heavily overfished, and at the north end of Lake Albert *Alestes baremose* has been overfished. It is essential to establish conservation measures as soon as possible and to ensure that these are enforced. This is not easy, as the fishermen are dispersed, but the introduction of new methods provides a chance to do so. Sea stocks have been overfished and one must beware of overfishing in man-made lakes.

Jackson's statement "the fecundity of tropical fish stocks, and their ability to withstand heavy fishing, is extremely high . . . few, if any, conservation regulations . . . should prove to be necessary" implies that fecundity is a major factor when framing conservation measures, whereas it is rarely of importance. For the majority of species there is no relationship between recruitment and stock density over a wide range of stock densities. For such species the aim of conservation measures is to obtain the maximum yield per recruit by limiting the amount of fishing to the optimum level. Fishing effort in excess of this will lead to a fall in the yield per recruit which is termed "overfishing". Fecundity has no relevance to this problem because recruitment is unaffected by the conservation measures required to obtain this yield. Species in this category "withstand heavy fishing" because the number of recruits is unaffected by fishing but the yield is less than that which could be taken if the stock were rationally fished. Garrod (*J. Cons. perm. int. Explor. Mer* (1961) **26(2)**) describes a typical example, that of *Tilapia esculenta* in Lake Victoria. A fishery in which the maximum yield per recruit is obtained can be considered "well-managed", to use Jackson's phrase, and because all fisheries eventually become overfished unless conserved, regulations are obviously necessary.

When fecundity is low the level of fishing at which the maximum yield per

recruit is obtained may be higher than that which will permit stock replace-
ment, in which case some loss in yield per recruit will have to be sustained in
order to maintain recruitment. For some species with high fecundity it may
be possible to fish the stock so effectively that recruitment is affected. The
Labeo species of East Africa, which are very vulnerable to capture as they
ascend rivers to spawn, are an example. A reduction in the number of recruits
directly attributable to fishing can be termed "biological overfishing" and it
would appear that Jackson is confusing this with "overfishing".

Fisheries conservation is often regarded as impractical because evasion is
usually easy but it must be the aim of the fisheries biologist to ensure rational
fishing if possible. There are two major advantages in attempting conservation measures in a new man-made lake. Firstly, it is possible during the period
of training which the indigenous people should receive during resettlement to
demonstrate the benefits of conservation as part of any fisheries course. This
will ensure that the fishermen are aware of the purposes of any conservation
regulations. Secondly, the fishermen will not be being asked to adopt any
measures which will lead to a drop in catches, which is usually the immediate
result of conservation measures in established fisheries.

The fisheries research biologist must predict before the lake forms what will
be the most valuable commercial species and determine sufficient of their
population dynamics to formulate conservation measures in advance. These
should be over-cautious because it is easier to relax regulations than impose
them.

P. B. N. JACKSON: I agree that it is possible to overfish fish stocks. The
point was that tropical fish can withstand a good deal of fishing.

HICKLING: Simple and effective breeding techniques have been evolved in
Formosa and India which allow of the breeding in captivity and in static
water of many species of river fish, including many species of *Labeo*, which are
usually considered to need flowing and well-oxygenated water for breeding,
and to make spawning migrations to do so. If therefore man-made impoundments genuinely bar normal fish movements which are undoubtedly for spawning purposes, re-stocking could be done by these fish-breeding techniques. In
mainland China the natural spawning of valuable fish seems no longer to be
relied on for re-stocking. A Japanese mission to China in 1964, which reported
early in 1965, states that in 1964 no fewer than 1 200 million fish fry were
artificially bred for re-stocking in China (according to a translated abstract
which I have).

Fish are very frequently seen to be leaping about in cascades and spillways
from artificial impoundments, but it has been shown that these fish may often
have undeveloped gonads; and I think it has to be proved in each case that
fish seen to be behaving in this way are attempting a necessary spawning
migration before contemplating the expense of remedial measures.

GWYNN: I would like to ask Mr. Jackson why he says the Tana River eels in
Kenya are doomed to extinction. Irrigation proposals for the Tana are still
under investigation. The interim report from FAO advises 200 cusec release

of water from every dam. It seems here that there has been a failure of communication between scientists and engineers. What is the value of the eels? Can they go up a fish pass?

P. B. N. JACKSON: If the barriers on the Tana are complete to the extent that water no longer flows down to the sea the eels will die; they can only survive if a minimum permissible flow is arrived at. Also, if there is no flow, conditions in the estuary may be adversely affected by silting and higher salinity, as has happened, for example, in some South African river mouths due to damming of too much fresh water higher up. I agree that at all times there should be consultation between biologists and engineers. I do not know what is the value of the eels, whether measured in monetary or other values, but imagine that, as once they are gone they are gone for ever, it is quite considerable. They can get up fish passes with great facility.

The Invasion of Man-made Lakes
by Plants

E. C. S. LITTLE

Weed Research Organization, Begbroke Hill, Oxford, England

INTRODUCTION

Most of the early large man-made lakes were formed in temperate regions for the generation of electricity. The altitude of the lakes and the general deepness of their water limited the opportunities for plants to occupy more than insignificant amounts of the new area of water.

Moreover the lakes were formed in relatively uninhabited areas where the plant communities had reached a balanced state with no plant forms available to exploit the ecological situation presented by the sudden appearance of a large area of deep water. Many big natural lakes exist which, apart from plants in the shallow margins, were mainly clear of vegetation. Thus it is not surprising that trouble from plants was scarcely anticipated and precautions against the risk of plant invasion were not taken.

If the water is deeper than about 30 ft, plants must float in order to establish themselves because there is insufficient light available in the depths to enable seeds that have germinated on the bottom to grow.

Completely free-floating vascular plants are rare compared with the myriad forms that live rooted in the soil. Two floating plants have caused most of the trouble in tropical lakes: the notorious water hyacinth *Eichhornia crassipes* Solms and the water fern *Salvinia auriculata* Aublet. Both are natives of South America where they are apparently of relatively little importance. A much lesser menace but sometimes an important invader is the water lettuce *Pistia stratiotes* L. All are important only in warm climates.

With the recent spectacular invasion of a number of new lakes by these plants, the dangers from such weeds have become apparent. Large masses of plants when floating at the mercy of the wind can threaten water channels leading into and out of a lake; they can impede or completely prevent navigation—an important benefit which a lake may provide.

A new lake may submerge large areas of agricultural land, but can as a substitute provide valuable fishing. Water weeds in dense mats may create deoxygenated conditions where fish cannot live and make fishing operations difficult or impossible.

Large volumes of water contained in a lake may be occupied and displaced by weeds. These plants will also promote loss of water by transpiration. Where the density of plants involved is small this reduction in the storage capacity of the lake can be ignored, but there is a degree of infestation where such losses demand remedial action. However, there is as yet insufficient information to determine when this critical degree is reached.

Where lakes are only 5–10 ft deep, the clearance of floating weeds from the surface may give submerged weeds an opportunity to take advantage of the light thus made available to them. Submerged plants can fill the water with tangled vegetation and impede fishing, navigation and recreation. Where the amount of stored water is directly valuable the amount displaced by these plants may be important. Submerged weeds are especially difficult to control and satisfactory methods of eliminating them are still being actively investigated.

Where the water is very shallow (less than 4 ft), many emergent weeds such as grasses, sedges and rushes can be expected. When there is a large rise and fall of the water this problem is seldom acute. Methods for the control of emergent plants are well known, but can be very expensive.

In situations in which it is obvious that money must be spent to remove invading plants from a lake considerable knowledge is available to assist in the choice of chemical or mechanical methods of clearance. But some research will always be advisable to ensure that the most economic method is adopted to suit the local conditions.

It may be advisable to spend money on research before a crisis develops and thus ensure that prompt and effective action is taken to prevent weeds becoming established. These may spread more rapidly and be more difficult to eradicate once seeds are produced.

The massive invasion of Lake Kariba by a floating plant showed that planning the construction of lakes, especially in the warmer regions of the planet, must include provisions to protect the water from losses and obstruction by plants.

This article outlines some of the weed problems on lakes. Methods by which they have been or could be dealt with are briefly mentioned.

Some Man-made Lakes Invaded by Plants

LAKE KARIBA

The explosive development of the water fern *Salvinia auriculata* on Lake Kariba is well known. Hattingh (1961) and Schelpe (1961) described how immediately the lake began to fill the first signs of invasion by weeds were observed. *Salvinia* had been present for some years in the Zambezi River; periodic floods had flushed the weed downstream. The relatively still water of the lake, however, provided ideal conditions for the plant to develop.

Boughey (1963) expanded these reports. He described the development of "sudd" communities in which the buoyancy of the *Salvinia* mats supports and promotes the growth of some forty species of vascular plants. He pointed out the danger that such intertwined masses of vegetation can present when moving before the wind or with the current. He reported that one such mass was caught in the crown of a submerged tree and was observed to snap off the trunk.

Fortunately on Lake Kariba the prevailing wind for almost every day of the year is upstream of the dam (Boughey, 1963), which reduces the chance of large masses of weed interfering with the dam installations.

No work to control the *Salvinia* on the lake has yet been attempted, though in 1963 Hattingh (unpublished report) obtained valuable information on the effectiveness of a range of herbicides. He has made recommendations which are still applicable though the present political situation has made direct action to deal with the *Salvinia* difficult.

Meanwhile D. S. Mitchell (personal communication) is continuing a careful study of the autecology of the plant. In 1964 he informed the writer that in 1962 the area occupied by the weed reached a peak of 400 sq. miles. The area now occupied by the plant appears to be declining to the still formidable amount of 200 sq. miles or 10% of the total lake surface.

This infestation occurring as it does over virtually the whole of the Zambezi system must, in the words of Boughey (1963), "constitute a threat to the rest of tropical and subtropical Africa and to further developmental projects such as the Volta scheme in Ghana".

The only bright aspect of this picture is that, as yet, *Eichhornia* has not been seen on Lake Kariba.

LAKE VOLTA

This huge lake in Ghana has just been completed, its 3 000 sq. miles making it much larger even than Lake Kariba. With the lesson of Lake Kariba before them the authorities in Ghana have arranged at an early stage for expert surveillance for any signs of similar plant invasions.

Fortunately Ghana like most of West Africa is still without infestations of either *E. crassipes* or *S. auriculata*. *Pistia stratiotes* is there and E. T. Heinen (personal communication) working for the Volta River Basin Executive Committee on water weed problems informed the writer in

1964 that only small colonies of *Pistia* had been observed on the lake. Thus this vast sheet of water, covering fertile land presumably rich in nutrients, lying in a warm climate is waiting for whatever plant invasion may swarm over it.

The recent discovery that *S. auriculata* has invaded the Congo River (Little, 1965) adds to the fears that the infestation of this weed may spread to West Africa and to the large new lakes there. The Congo has also for some years been heavily infested with *E. crassipes*, and floating masses of these two plants, if they reach the sea, may be accidentally or deliberately carried to eastern West Africa—one of the few tropical regions of the planet so far free of this weed. *E. crassipes* appeared in Senegal in 1964 (*Pl. Prot. Bull. FAO*, 1964).

THE WHITE NILE

The Jebel Auliya Dam on the White Nile, which is 30 miles upstream from the confluence of the White and Blue Niles at Khartoum, forms a shallow lake to store water for irrigation. Heinen and Hassan Ahmed (1964) have described the efforts made by the Sudan Government to control the heavy infestation of *E. crassipes* on the river and to check the weed from spreading downstream past the dam. A staff of 200 people is employed in this task equipped with land spraying machines, boats and aircraft. The sum of about £500 000 is being spent each year on keeping the river open and holding the infestation within the White Nile. In spite of all efforts, some hyacinth plants have been detected and destroyed below the Jebel Auliya Dam. There is thus the risk of the infestation spreading into the Blue Nile and thence into the Gezira cotton scheme channels and downstream into the new great lake to be formed behind the Aswan Dam. The authorities are fully alive to the threat and every effort is being made to seek out and destroy any plants or seedlings of hyacinth which penetrate the Jebel Auliya Dam to the lower reaches of the river. Further assistance for research into this international problem is being sought.

LAKE APANÁS

This small lake (16 sq. miles) in Nicaragua provides a good example of the type of weed problem which may well develop in man-made lakes as more rivers in tropical regions are harnessed for power and irrigation.

The lake was only filled in 1964. By June 1965 a large population of water hyacinth and *Pistia* had developed (estimated to cover about 250 acres), and it was clear, to the writer, that the hyacinth was spreading rapidly. While the authorities were showing some anxiety and had made a number of inquiries as to how the weeds could be controlled, no action to control the infestation had been taken. It was interesting to see that at one end (N.E.) of the long winding lake only hyacinth was present, while at the other (S.W.) there was only *Pistia*. In the middle regions mixtures of the two weeds occurred.

"Sudd" formation with grass and other plants was taking place only in the hyacinth region. Both the narrow channel of the intake to the turbines and the spillway overflow tunnel seemed to be vulnerable to blockage should large islands of matted weeds be formed and detached by high winds. When the authorities realized that these hazards presented real threats to the project, plans were made for controlling the infestation by conventional means.

LAKE RIO LEMPA

This project in El Salvador is similar to that of Lake Apanás, though somewhat larger. However, the lake has existed for eight years and in that time the water hyacinth which grows densely all round the lake has never given any trouble to the engineers. The overflow system of the project consists of a simple spillway over the dam. Thus the hyacinth which piles up against the dam is periodically flushed over the dam by flood waters and carried away to the sea. The openings of the penstocks are well below the level of the water and are heavily screened against blockage, so the authorities appear justified in claiming that the weed does the project no harm. However, there seem to be questions which engineers should be able to answer precisely before they tolerate a notorious weed like hyacinth spreading freely over their project.

(a) What effect do large masses of vegetation such as hyacinth have on the evaporation losses of the lake? How much water is lost in this way and what is it worth?

(b) What proportion of the effective volume of water above the penstocks does the mass of weed displace? What is the value of this water?

It was surprising to find at both Lake Apanás and Rio Lempa that there was little appreciation of the need to answer these questions. The water losses depend on wide variables of temperature, wind velocity and size and type of plants concerned and this needs to be determined for each site. One engineer was met who considered that plants covering a water surface should reduce water losses. However, one publication (Penfound and Earle, 1948) reports that water hyacinth could increase evaporation losses up to six times normal. When a typical evaporation rate from a lake surface may be 4 ft per annum (Parsons, 1949), it is clear that six times this loss would be of the highest importance. Thus there seems to be an urgent need for engineers at each lake project to carry out simple evaporation measurements in watertight tanks comparing typical water weed infestations with tanks containing water only.

The other question of displacement should be more easily answered. Once the space occupied by the weed on the lake is mapped and the average weight of the plants per unit area is determined, then the volume of water displaced can be calculated. A dense mat of hyacinth could weigh about 500 lb/sq. yd which involves a displacement of about 1 ft of water. This would represent 3% of the utilizable water (33 ft) above the penstocks on Lake Rio Lempa and more in shallower parts of the lake. Since the area of hyacinth on this lake may be 1 000 acres, the mere presence of the weed represents a loss of 1 000 acres/ft of water.

In addition there are the less easily measured losses to fish and fishing. The recreational facilities are also impaired.

These factors may induce authorities responsible for lakes infested with water hyacinth to decide that to control water weeds to an acceptable level may well be worth while on economic grounds; apart from any hazards which the weed presents to the project itself.

BROKOPONDO RESERVOIR, SURINAM

A survey in 1964 (L. W. Weldon, unpublished report) of this reservoir which has an area of about 600 sq. miles showed that a large area of the lake (about 12 sq. miles) was infested in varying degrees with hyacinth.

This and all the other lakes mentioned above other than Lake Kariba are apparently free from S. auriculata.

SOUTHERN STATES OF U.S.A.

Extensive works carried out in the Southern States of the U.S.A. have created many lakes and controlled and channelled many waterways. Here hyacinth has caused tremendous difficulties, but the energy and resources available have succeeded in clearing large areas of the weed both by mechanical methods and by chemical treatments (Wunderlich, 1964; Robinson, 1965). In some areas (in Louisiana) the results have been so successful that there is hope that extermination may have been achieved. However, the ability of hyacinth seed to remain dormant and germinate when disturbed after long periods make it seem unlikely that vigilance can be safely relaxed from any area once infested. A serious complication is the development of another weed not so far particularly troublesome elsewhere, Alternanthera philoxeroides (Mart.) Griseb., known in the U.S.A. as alligator weed. There is, however, a recent report of the introduction of this weed in India (Maheshwari, 1965). This weed is successful because in addition to a vigorous reproductive capacity it is resistant to herbicides. This resistance is mainly due to dormant buds which are exceptionally difficult to kill.

Submerged weeds also are testing the ingenuity and skill of research workers in the U.S.A.

To destroy mechanically or chemically a plant growing up from the bottom of several feet of water, at an economic cost, without harming fish presents an interesting problem, especially when this is further complicated by residues of trees and shrubs left to be submerged by the rising water of the lake. *Elodea* spp. are particularly troublesome with many others, including *Najas, Myriophyllum,* contributing to the problem. At present no clear answer is in sight.

If fish can be sacrificed then acrolein makes an effective clearance of all submerged weeds. Techniques for injecting this rather hazardous substance into infested lakes and waterways are being perfected (Seabrook, 1965).

An approach finding favour in the U.S.A. is to fertilize the lake water to promote a bloom of algae and other micro-organisms of a density such as to prevent submerged weeds from growing by excluding light. This method is obviously only practicable on small lakes.

METHODS OF CONTROL

MECHANICAL

Mechanical methods of control including cutting by hand and by machines, evacuating by draglines and the use of special saw boats (as developed in the U.S.A.) have limited practical use, and usually are prohibitively expensive.

Where large areas of weeds have to be controlled by the most economical method there is no alternative at present but to use herbicides.

CHEMICAL

Fortunately the worst weed of all, hyacinth, is relatively susceptible to 2,4-D (Harrison, 1964) so large quantities of this compound are used to destroy hyacinth in many parts of the world (Heinen and Hassan Ahmed, 1964). *Salvinia* has been shown to be effectively controlled by paraquat (Hattingh, unpublished reports). *Pistia* can be controlled by 2,4-D but current recommendations favour diquat (Harrison, 1964). The same publication recommends the use of fenoprop (silvex) for *Alternanthera,* but the rate required (8 lb/acre) and the need for repeat spraying is so expensive as to indicate the need for further research.

There are no methods as yet available by which submerged weeds like *Elodea* can be cheaply and effectively destroyed without toxic effects on fish. Fishing and the interests of anglers are features which contribute to the difficulties of the use of herbicides. Fortunately the most important chemical, 2,4-D, is relatively harmless to fish.

However, 2,4-D can damage many important crops (cotton is extremely sensitive). Other water weed herbicides have also to be used with great care on water surrounded by agricultural areas. Fortunately most of the new lakes are still not extensively developed along their margins which gives greater freedom to herbicide applicators, especially when aerial spraying is used. Aerial spraying usually provides the quickest and most efficient method of distributing herbicides, so methods to limit the risk of drift which may travel to susceptible crops are being studied (Little *et al.*, 1964).

BIOLOGICAL

Chemical and mechanical control of water weeds presents such a depressing picture of continuing costs every year, with the justifiable fear that even when one weed has been exterminated it will be replaced by another which may be even more difficult and expensive to control, that it is not surprising that the possibility of some form of biological control of weeds being effective offers a tantalizingly attractive prospect to many people. This form of control is even more sought after by developing countries with far fewer resources than the U.S.A.

Thus the possibility of using the manatee, a harmless large mammal which eats large quantities of most water weeds (Allsopp, 1960, 1961), has intensely interested many people. Unfortunately it is generally recognized that the manatee idea is impracticable in our present state of knowledge. Almost nothing is known of the physiology of the animal except that its breeding is slow and erratic. Methods of easy handling of vigorous creatures weighing up to a ton have not yet been evolved. Also the animals are highly vulnerable to destruction by man himself for meat or for sport.

Fortunately some action to study the manatee more closely is under way, financed by the Florida Flood Control Committee (Sguros, 1965). But it seems likely that long and expensive research may be needed before there is any likelihood of manatees being useful in other than very specialized areas.

Other forms of biological control of water weeds include the use of snails, of which *Marisa cornuarietis* (Seaman and Porterfield, 1964) carries the hopes of several workers. Studies of this mollusc are currently in progress both at the U.S. Public Health service in Puerto Rico and at the U.S. Department of Agriculture at Fort Lauderdale, Florida. It seems optimistic to hope that this snail can contend with the massive problem of water weeds because predators and other causes may keep any snail population below the large numbers needed to deal with the mass of plant material represented by typical hyacinth infestations.

Various insects are also being tested against water weeds and there is always the chance some successful introductions may be achieved against individual plant species. But there is little hope that insects can deal with any submerged weeds or mixed populations of emerged plants. The possibilities of fish being used for water weed control is also being explored. Though herbivorous fish seem promising, especially against submerged weeds, there is little evidence as yet that substantial results from their use can be expected, again because of losses to predators.

DISCUSSION AND CONCLUSIONS

Examples of man-made lakes with serious water weed problems have been given, but there are lakes in warm conditions where no water weeds of any consequence have ever developed. An example is the Hermitage reservoir in Jamaica which was formed in 1960 but which as yet has never had any weeds in it other than some algae. The lake may be free either because it has steep banks, and flushes itself periodically over the spillway, or because no one has yet introduced water hyacinth which grows freely elsewhere in the island, or there may be something about the lake which inhibits weed growth. Answers to these questions are not known but they are matters which are of considerable interest and anxiety to engineers who have the responsibility for the maintenance of this lake and the construction of others on the island (D. A. Davies, personal communication).

The small (about 500 acres) man-made Inya (once Victoria) lake in Rangoon, Burma, presented a particularly interesting problem to the writer between 1960–62. Small infestations of water hyacinths in channels round the margin repeatedly released plants into the lake. But for some unexplained reason these plants never developed an infestation, and the lake remained clear of the weed in spite of apparently ideal growing conditions.

Opinions are often expressed that large lakes, such as the Volta, are sure to be infested sooner or later with water hyacinth and other weeds because there is no means of stopping irresponsible or ignorant people from spreading plants like *Eichhornia*, *Salvinia* and *Elodea* which have long been popular in ornamental ponds and aquaria. It was reported to the writer in Florida that some fishermen had objected to the clearance of hyacinth from their lakes because they believe that a certain amount of these plants provide useful shelter for fish. Threats had been expressed that if the authorities succeeded in their plans for the elimination of this weed, the fishermen would reintroduce it!

This irresponsible attitude compounds the difficulties of those who

D

realize that aquatic weeds present a serious threat to one of mankind's most important needs for agricultural and industrial development— ample water. As countries progress towards further development, more and more areas of water will be impounded and channelled. To conserve this water and to deliver and drain it swiftly and effectively is vital to progress. Some water plants are seriously challenging man's ability to do this. It is, therefore, clear that improved, cheaper and swifter methods of keeping water weeds under control must be sought. These studies should include not only improved chemical and mechanical means of attack, but also fundamental studies of the biology of these plants so that weaknesses may be discovered in their amazing capacity to reproduce and occupy large areas of water in a short time.

Biological methods of control should be fully explored since such methods could be the most economical. There is always the possibility that in some situations water weeds could be exploited profitably (Pirie, 1960).

All these questions point to the need for research. It is surprising that relatively so little intensive effort to solve the problems of aquatic weeds is being carried out; with no research on this subject in progress on an international scale. Research appears particularly needed into the ecological limitations of each of the most important weeds, especially the part played by the water in which they grow and the effect of climate. Such work would provide an invaluable foundation on which predictions as to the likelihood of infestations on new lakes could be based. *Eichhornia, Salvinia, Elodea, Pistia* and others are plants causing loss and hardship to millions of people in many countries, and their potential for harm is far from being fully reached. A combined international campaign, financed perhaps by the United Nations, to contest them is needed to protect and conserve much of the water resources of the world. The international conference on aquatic weed control held at La Rochelle in 1964 is a first step in the right direction.

REFERENCES

Allsopp, W. H. L. (1960). The manatee: ecology and use for weed control. *Nature, Lond.* **188**, 762.
Allsopp, W. H. L. (1961). Putting manatees to work. *New Scient.* No. 263, 548–549.
Boughey, A. S. (1963). The explosive development of a floating weed vegetation on Lake Kariba. *Adansonia* **3**, 49–61.
FAO Plant Protection Bulletin. (1964). Occurrence of water hyacinth in Senegal. **12**(4), 93.
Harrison, D. S. (1964). Aquatic weed control. University of Florida Agricultural Extension Service, Circular 219A.

Hattingh, E. R. (1961). The problem of *Salvinia auriculata* Aubl. and associated aquatic weeds on Kariba Lake. *Weed Res.* **1**, 303–306.

Heinen, E. T. and Hassan Ahmed (1964). Water hyacinth control on the Nile river. Sudan Department of Agriculture, Khartoum.

Little, E. C. S. (1965). The discovery of *Salvinia auriculata* on the Congo. *Nature, Lond.* **208**, 1111–1112.

Little, E. C. S. and Robson, T. O. and Johnstone, D. R. (1964). A report on a project for drift free aerial spraying of water weeds. Proceedings 7th British Weed Control Conference, pp. 920–924.

Maheshwari, J. K. (1965). Alligator weed in Indian lakes. *Nature, Lond.* **206**, 1270.

Parsons, D. A. (1949). Hydrology of a small area near Auburn, Alabama. U.S. Department of Agriculture Soil Conservancy Service, T.P. 85.

Penfound, W. T. and Earle, T. T. (1948). The biology of the water hyacinth. *Ecol. Monogr.* **18**, 447–472.

Pirie, N. W. (1960). Water hyacinth: a curse or a crop? *Nature, Lond.* **185**, 116.

Robinson, P. E. (1965). Dam B reservoir water hyacinth control. Proceedings 18th Southern Weed Control Conference, pp. 464–468.

Schelpe, E. A. C. L. E. (1961). The ecology of *Salvinia auriculata* and associated vegetation on Kariba Lake. *J. S. Afr. Bot.* **27**, 181–187.

Seabrook, E. (1965). Use of acrolein for control of *Elodea*. *Hyacinth Cont. J.* **4**. (In press).

Seaman, D. E. and Porterfield, W. A. (1964). Control of aquatic weeds by the snail *Marisa cornuarietis*. *Weeds* **12**, 87–92.

Sguros, P. (1965). Use of manatees for aquatic weed control. *Hyacinth Cont. J.* **4**. (In press).

Symposium International sur les Moyens de Destruction des Plantes Aquatiques, La Rochelle, France (1964). (In press). (Reviewed in *Weed Res.* (1965) **5**, 185–186.)

Wunderlich, W. E. (1964). Water hyacinth control in Louisiana. *Hyacinth Cont. J.* **3**, 4–7.

Discussion

SMITH: It may be relevant to Dr. Little's query about water loss from floating weeds to refer to work done in Hawaii showing high water losses from rice crops.

FORD: Transpiration losses from rice crops are indeed higher than from water surface evaporation and are a significant factor in provision of irrigation water. In further reply to Dr. Little's query, a possible illustration would be that of a fairly shallow water supply reservoir in the tropics designed to supply 50 m.g.d., of area such that the loss from normal surface evaporation averaged 8 m.g.d.; if the surface were covered by weed and if (as suggested on p. 79) evapo-transpiration were then as much as six times this, the water loss would be 48 m.g.d. which would clearly be serious.

GILSON: Dr. Little has not mentioned *Papyrus* which I have always understood was a trouble maker.

LITTLE: *Papyrus* is a serious weed which is the basis of the Nile sudd. Professor Ewer referred to it as a potential danger.

DE BONT: Concerning evaporation from lakes with and without a floating plant cover, the data mentioned here are not sufficient to conclude whether or not there is a difference between man-made lakes with and without plant mats. The total amount of water backed up by a dam consists partly of ground water. If the extent and amount of this ground water is not the same for the covered and open lake, direct observations of change in level and of rate of inflow and outflow are not sufficient to answer this question.

HICKLING: Correspondence with a Chinese colleague suggests that water-weeds have so far been no problem in China because the swamps and shallower waters are used for rice cultivation, and the slightly deeper static waters for the intensive cultivation of aquatic crops such as water chestnut, water-cress, *Sagittaria* roots, Lotus, *Ipomaea aquatica*, *Zizania aquatica*, etc. In addition, and more important, the Chinese fish fauna includes the white amur or grass carp, *Ctenopharyngodon idella* Val., which is probably the most effective of all weed-eating fish. As to *Eichhornia* and *Pistia*, there are no complaints as these are eagerly sought by duck and pig farmers as a useful fodder.

BERTRAM: Dr. Little has rightly said that "unfortunately it is generally recognized that the manatee idea (for the control of aquatic vegetation) is unpracticable in our present state of knowledge". My wife and I have investigated in recent years the status and biology of sirenians, both manatees and dugongs. We would add further perspective to what Dr. Little says.

Manatees, indeed, may have great theoretical potentiality for use as weed clearers in tropical fresh waters, but as yet any such scheme is quite unpractical on a numerical basis. The manatee is a rare animal and difficult to catch, and that applies to both sides of the Atlantic. Further, as yet breeding has not been brought about under "weed clearance conditions" so that each experiment involves the virtual sterilization of further rare animals. Additional queries are whether manatees will in fact eat *Salvinia*, and whether they will eat vegetation floating in deep water. There is great scope for further investigation, and the efforts of the Florida Flood Control organization are to be commended. Ideally, manatees would be brought to breed freely in the process of their weed clearance, and then they might be harvested for useful meat in addition.

The dugongs, on the other hand, are totally marine mammals, but in certain regions of the northern coasts of Australia and in Torres Strait they are relatively abundant, though now becoming rare elsewhere throughout their range. Those concerned with certain developments in the Northern Territory of Australia in connexion with rice growing presently have an interest in weed control in certain small freshwater areas. They propose to experiment with dugongs to see if, as they might, they will survive and work helpfully in such fresh waters. If they do survive, and do significantly consume freshwater vegetation, and yet do not breed in fresh water, there may well be wild dugongs enough to stand a substantial harvesting from the sea for use in lakes and channels.

Medical Problems Arising from the Making of
Lakes in the Tropics

B. B. WADDY

London School of Hygiene and Tropical Medicine, London, England

INTRODUCTION

Growing needs in tropical countries for water conservation, hydro-electric power and national prestige are resulting in the building of large dams. At least in Africa, which is generally a flat country, the lakes created tend to spread out for many miles laterally and a very long distance along the original course of the river dammed. The greatest lateral spread probably will be seen above the Egyptian High Dam, for at Wadi Halfa the land appears to be absolutely flat for miles to the east of the Nile. In Ghana, the Volta Lake will extend some 200 miles upstream of the dam, along the Volta itself, its constituent rivers the Black and White Voltas and one or two main tributaries.

A lake such as that above the High Dam will provide such a tremendous surface area for evaporation that the climate of the region may be affected. This may affect the prevalence of certain diseases, in the epidemiology of which aerial humidity is important. The effects, if any, will be beneficial rather than the reverse: this is obviously speculative, and having been mentioned, it will not be considered further.

Apart from this, the problems arising from the making of lakes are in two categories, human and zoological.

Human beings first are gathered together in large numbers as a labour force to build the dam. A population density, such as the area may never have seen before, offers opportunities and facilities for the transmission of communicable diseases, the whole prevalence of which in the area may be permanently affected. When the lake fills, riparian people must move away from their former homes—it is to be hoped according to an orderly plan.

The substitution of a large, static, seasonally fluctuating stretch of water for a flowing river radically alters the suitability of the area to maintain the intermediate hosts of certain very important diseases.

87

Human Aspects

BUILDING THE DAM

After all the preliminaries of conducting a feasibility survey and signing contracts have been completed, the main construction work will probably occupy about five years. The labour force builds up to roughly 1 000 technicians (the great majority expatriates) and 10 000 unskilled labourers. An annual turnover of about 30% can be expected in the unskilled labour force, and the contractors will be lucky if the turnover in their expatriate labour force is much less.

In the last fifteen years, there has been a change in the attitude of employers to labour, in this sort of public work in the tropics. Formerly, local labourers were housed in ways that would hardly be used for cattle and many of the expatriate technicians fared little better—nor did they expect to. Then the Preparatory Commission for the Volta River Project (Report, 1956) gave very careful consideration to the welfare of its prospective labour force. Work on the Volta Dam did not commence for some years, but at Kariba, Rhodesia (constructed 1956–59 inclusive) the principle of treating the labour force as fellow human beings was actually put into effect (Webster, 1960).

From the epidemiological viewpoint, the main difference is that under the new idea, men are encouraged by the conditions they find to bring their wives and children to join them. Thus the transmission of certain bachelors' and grass-widowers' diseases is reduced, but the population of the construction camp—or rather township—is more than doubled. Moreover, families are more susceptible to communicable disease, and less controllable, than the labourers themselves.

In addition to the labour force itself, many other categories of person are attracted to the area: traders (large and small), daughters of joy, beggars and (most of all) itinerant labourers looking for work but failing to get it. These last, and also labourers who are discharged as unfit to work, amount to a considerable body of very unhealthy men. They have no money, with which to travel home, and inevitably they remain as beggars.

Thus, in the course of a year or two, a population of perhaps 25 000 builds up in the controlled construction zone. They are well housed and under some sanitary control, but the population density is high and they are in contact with all the riverine vectors of disease. Just outside the construction zone, where the main road enters it, some unfortunate village inevitably becomes a boom town, filled with human flotsam and jetsam. In the area of the Niger Dam, Nigeria, the village to suffer is called Wawa. Its population was a few hundred, and the fact that it had no sanitation was not particularly important. But who knows how many people are living in Wawa now? They literally carpet the ground at night, and their waste products are piled high in every borrow pit. Clearly they represent a new and serious health hazard in an area in which the former population density was perhaps twenty to the square mile. The spread of dysentery and epidemic disease into the construction township, and into the surrounding area (which probably has only exiguous medical services) would have disastrous results.

The Preparatory Commission of the Volta Dam anticipated this situation. The solution proposed, which may or may not have been put into practice, was that the Dam Authority (the existence of which, after all, was responsible for drawing people to the area) should be responsible for repatriating all those who were, or became, unfit to work on the dam. No doubt the interpretation of this would be elastic, but the total cost would be small in relation to the £80–120 million cost of building the dam.

Hazards to the health of expatriate technicians and their families are of relatively little public health importance, and deserve mention only because they may interfere with the building of the dam. Malaria is usually the greatest of them, especially since the fashion of installing water-borne sanitation must reduce the transmission of intestinal infections to a low level. In Africa, schistosomiasis and onchocerciasis are two serious menaces. Schistosomiasis, a helminthic disease of which the intermediate host is a water snail, causes several weeks' incapacitation of any non-immune adult infected for the first time. It is not feared nearly enough. On the other hand, onchocerciasis caused by a filarial worm and carried by blackflies (*Simulium* spp.) is feared far too much. It is known, all too well, that in hyperendemic foci of onchocerciasis 10% or more of the population may be blind. The expatriate worker, or his wife, often expecting to go blind the day after his first blackfly bite, may simply refuse to carry on with the job in the presence of blackflies. Vector-borne diseases will be considered in greater detail below.

RESETTLEMENT PROBLEMS

In relation to the size of the man-made lakes, at least in Africa, the numbers of people displaced by them are small. The Volta Lake displaces some 70 000, and the Niger Lake a similar number. The Egyptian High Dam displaces 80 000 people from Wadi Halfa and a few thousand more from Egyptian villages. Further afield, in time and place, the lakes of the Suez and Panama canals were formed in almost uninhabited country. Nevertheless, a problem of resettlement and welfare is created.

Whatever plans are made for resettlement, some of the people displaced merely retreat as the water rises, to live as before on the water's edge.

Some are farmers, who may find land for themselves, or may be found land. They cannot be directed where to settle: all that can be done is to provide water supplies and roads to the places where settlement seems most desirable. Others are glad to settle in a new town. This may be built in close association with the construction township, making use of established amenities such as the hospital and shopping area. New Bussa, to replace the Bussa that will sink below the Niger Lake, is an example. If hydro-electric power is to be used locally, a town of considerable size will absorb displaced population and much immigrant labour as well. This will happen if aluminium smelting is established near the Volta Lake. Jinja, beside the Owen Falls Dam at the source of the White Nile from Lake Victoria, is a large and flourishing town.

The hazard to health involved is that of vector-borne diseases, transmitted more intensely than they were before the population density increased. The dam labour force, gathered together from a wide area, will already have introduced every possible endemic disease. During the construction phase, active vector control measures will have kept down transmission, but these measures are usually too expensive for permanent maintenance.

The farmers who are to be displaced must be convinced of the fact well in advance. If they are not, there will be a year of famine, when farms planted in the valley will be inundated and there will be no possibility of planting again higher up. This happened to a number of communities displaced as the Kariba (Zambezi) lake filled. Primitive agricultural communities usually have some "last resort" food, wild fruit or nuts, to which to turn in famine years. In the Zambezi valley certain roots were eaten in case of famine. The displaced farming families resorted to these, not realizing that, growing up in the hills, they were not identical with those in the valley. They did, in fact, contain certain active principles similar to those in the ackee apple, depressing blood sugar and producing the syndrome known as the vomiting sickness of Jamaica (Hill, 1959). Webster (1960), who described the medical aspects of building the Kariba Dam, recalled this occurrence in a conversation which it is hoped has been remembered correctly (see Gadd et al., 1962).

So far, only what is essentially local displacement has been considered. The Wadi Halfa area, however, is so flat that its population must be removed to a completely different environment. People in this area are undernourished, and have low average haemoglobins as a result. Where they are, they are subject to schistosomiasis, but not to the insect-borne diseases. The intention is to remove them to Khashm el Girba, in relation to the Atbara river. Here, for the first time, they will be at risk of malaria, kala azar and other diseases. Twenty-five years ago, the notorious African vector of malaria, *Anopheles gambiae*, did spread along the Nile and reached Lower Egypt. The desert people, with their low haemoglobins and their lack of immunity, died like flies. During this epidemic, in 1942, the monthly death rates per thousand at Abu Simbel were: January 3·4, February 1·4, March 13·1, April 18·3, and May 34·1.

The prospects for the Wadi Halfa people, after their move, will depend very much on malaria control. Otherwise, they should benefit by the move. Wadi Halfa is not a healthy place in which to live (Waddy, 1962).

ZOOLOGICAL ASPECTS

The important effects of altering the balance of nature are those affecting the intermediate hosts of human diseases, which may be considered in turn.

MALARIA

"The association of malaria epidemics with migrant labour, the epidemics occurring amongst labourers and local residents, is sufficiently well known to be honoured with a name of its own, malaria of tropical aggregation of labour." (Macdonald, 1957). Wherever malaria is potentially epidemic, the very introduction of an immigrant population may be enough by itself to disturb the balance. Perhaps the best known example of malaria in relation to man-made water systems is provided by the failure of de Lesseps to build the Panama Canal (in which Gatun Lake is not much smaller than the Lake of Geneva). The figures for sickness given by Scott (1939) are: a total of 86 800 men was taken into employment; 52 814 were treated for illness and 5 627 died. These figures by themselves suggest that causes other than medical ones were at least partly responsible for the failure of the project. It is interesting to note that medical expenditure in this ill-fated venture amounted to 0·5% of total expenditure, precisely the same figure as that given by Webster (1960) for the Kariba Dam project. The control of malaria in a labour force is now a straightforward routine affair. The important point to consider is the long-term effect of creating the lake. The first serious consideration of this problem, and its solution, was made in relation to the Tennessee Valley development project. There, the malaria vector was *Anopheles quadrimaculatus*, and its breeding was controlled successfully by raising and lowering the levels of lakes by about 1 ft every 7–10 days throughout the summer (Martin, 1956).

In due course, the same solution was proposed in connexion with the Volta Lake. The length of the latter, when full, being 200 miles, the idea was unkindly received by engineers. It was killed when local malariologists pointed out that, unlike *A. quadrimaculatus*, the African vector *A.*

D*

gambiae would be greatly encouraged by the measure (Macdonald, 1955). In fact, in West Africa malaria generally is holoendemic. Additional mosquitoes make little practical difference; at least lethal epidemics of malaria do not result from the carelessness of engineers, as they may do in the East.

ONCHOCERCIASIS

Onchocerciasis is caused by the filarial worm *Onchocerca volvulus*, transmitted from man to man by the bites of *Simulium* spp. The disease occurs in tropical Africa, Central America and Venezuela. The fly is much more widely distributed than the disease, and in its own right is one of the worst insect pests in the world. Onchocerciasis and its diabolical little vector must always be thought of in company. *Simulium* spp. breed in running, and therefore highly oxygenated, water. They are, therefore, most likely to be found at points on a river suitable for damming operations. The creation of a lake, rendering the water above it static, prevents the breeding of blackflies, though they may breed in spillways.

The building of the Owen Falls Dam was more or less brought to a standstill by the labour force retreating from the attentions of swarms of *Simulium damnosum*, the aptly named principal vector of onchocerciasis in Africa. In order to continue the work, it was necessary to eliminate the fly by dosing the White Nile with DDT, to which the larval forms of all *Simulium* spp. are intensely susceptible. This was done, and *S. damnosum* disappeared from the river for a long distance downstream. Provision for repeating the treatment, if it becomes necessary, is actually built into the dam structure. The result of the operation was not only relief for the dam builders. The country around the river downstream, which had been virtually uninhabited, was soon resettled and put to good use again (Brown, 1962).

This was a relatively simple and inexpensive operation, which produced spectacular benefits. The Volta Lake, too, will eliminate the breeding of *S. damnosum* permanently for a long way up-country, though not so far as to affect the hyperendemic onchocerciasis foci of northern Ghana. The river is being dosed with DDT periodically during the construction period (Hughes, 1964). In Nigeria, the situation around the area of the Niger Dam is complicated by the existence of tributaries in which *S. damnosum* also breeds. It was always agreed that, for this dam to be built, *S. damnosum* control was an essential prerequisite. Control has been carried out, successfully, but only by spreading control operations over a large area. They have been correspondingly costly.

Although the Niger itself will cease to breed *S. damnosum* for a long distance above the dam, there will remain many admirable breeding points in the main river downstream and in the tributaries. Matters will be no different from what they were formerly, except that the transmission of onchocerciasis will be far more favoured by a higher population density, part of it made up of already infected immigrants. The thought is somewhat disquieting.

SCHISTOSOMIASIS

The intermediate hosts of *Schistosoma haematobium* and *S. mansoni* are small water snails of the genera respectively of *Bulinus* and *Biomphalaria*. The schistosome miracidium, that hatches from the egg passed in human urine or faeces, must swim to find a snail. The cercaria that emerges later on from the snail must swim to find a human host. Obviously, the transmission of schistosomiasis depends on high densities of human beings and snails mingling together in static or sluggishly flowing water.

Ideal conditions for the introduction of schistosomiasis into an area might very easily be created by actual dam building operations. In Africa, a high proportion of the immigrant labourers would be infected. So far, in the Volta Dam (Hughes, 1964) and Niger Dam construction areas, the appropriate snails have not been found. But when a lake spreads out, almost certainly snails will multiply near its verges. At certain human gathering points, schistosomiasis transmission will take place. Schistosomiasis is more and more being recognized as a very dangerous disease to the individual, as well as a public health menace. It can only be hoped that future vigilance will be sufficient to prevent the disease from becoming hyperendemic in new foci.

CONCLUSION

The most important health hazards in connexion with the creation of lakes have been described briefly. As usual, there are more hazards in Africa than elsewhere. This is not simply because the few men who have written on the subject have Africa as their background. Though the African adult suffers less from malaria than other tropical dwellers, this is solely because—due to intense transmission—the adult is one of the survivors who was not killed by the disease in infancy. For other vector-borne diseases, Africa is the ideal environment and (in most instances) original source.

Water and good communications are fundamentals of public health, both provided by lakes. Protein supplies are increased in the form of fish. The amount of land lost, formerly in active use, is usually small, and land may be freed for agricultural use by the elimination of *Simulium* breeding. On the other side, the risk of spreading schistosomiasis may be increased. Nevertheless, putting both sides in the scales, who can doubt that the creation of a lake is a beneficial as well as a thrilling human action.

REFERENCES

Brown, A. W. A. (1962). A survey of *Simulium* control in Africa. *Bull. Wld Hlth Org.* **27**, 511.
Gadd, K. G., Nixon, L. C., Taube, E. and Webster, M. H. (1962). The Lusitu tragedy. *Cent. Afr. J. Med.* 8(12), Suppl.
Hill, K. R. (1959). Some observations on liver disease in the West Indies. *Trans. R. Soc. trop. Med. Hyg.* **53**, 217.
Hughes, J. P. (1964). Health aspects of the Volta River Project in Ghana. "Industry and Tropical Health", Vol. 5, p. 43. Boston. Harvard.
Macdonald, G. (1955). Medical implications of the Volta River Project. *Trans. R. Soc. trop. Med. Hyg.* **49**, 13.
Macdonald, G. (1957). "The Epidemiology and Control of Malaria." Oxford University Press, London.
Martin, R. C. (1956). "TVA. The First Twenty Years." Kingsport, Tennessee.
Scott, H. H. (1939). "A History of Tropical Medicine." Arnold, London.
Volta River Preparatory Commission (1956). "The Volta River Project." HMSO, London.
Waddy, B. B. (1962). The present state of public health in the African Soudan. *Trans. R. Soc. trop. Med. Hyg.* **56**, 95.
Webster, M. H. (1960). The medical aspects of the Kariba Hydro-Electric Scheme. *Cent. Afr. J. Med.* **6**, (10) Suppl.

The *Simulium* Problem and Fishery Development in the Proposed Niger Lake

W. E. KERSHAW*

Liverpool School of Tropical Medicine, Liverpool, England

The parasite *Onchocerca* in man and its vector *Simulium* whose larval and pupal forms live in fast-running water have an important bearing on the project to dam the waters of the Niger and produce a lake over Foge Island. The comments I propose to make are derived from observations made by my colleagues and me in the Kainji Biological Research Team organized by Dr. E. White. I wish first to discuss the relation of *Simulium* to man, then its relation to the development of fisheries in the lake.

Surveys by clinical examination and by skin snips at the villages of Shagunu, Swashi (on the banks of the River Swashi, a tributary of the Niger) and at Amboshidi, 5 miles south of Shagunu, showed that most people were infected with onchocerciasis. Many had a high intensity of infection and some had eye changes. From these surveys it was clear that those who remained solely in the village were lightly infected, and a few were not infected; those who fished for most of their time were also lightly infected; those who farmed, particularly near the Swashi, were heavily infected; and those who fished and farmed, as many did, were moderately infected. Fishing *per se* is not to be regarded as carrying the hazard of onchocerciasis.

The people in these villages have not been reached by the established medical facilities and require the organization of a rural medical service for their treatment, although there is a hospital at Kainji which has been established to provide a medical service for construction workers. When these villagers are resettled to other sites as the lake waters begin to rise, they will take with them their infection, and it is hard to believe that wherever they go in this area the vector will not be present to continue transmission. There was no difficulty in finding the aquatic stages of *Simulium damnosum* (the vector of onchocerciasis), nor in finding biting adult flies near Swashi and Shagunu, although DDT had been used for some weeks in the larger tributaries of the Niger, including the Swashi. The workers at the dam site at Kainji are well protected from the bites of *Simulium*, both as a vector of onchocerciasis and as a biting pest, because

*Present address: University of Salford, England.

95

of the splendid and tireless efforts of Mr. Goegny who, with the advice and help of Dr. B. B. Waddy of the London School of Hygiene and Tropical Medicine, has poured large quantities of soluble DDT into the larger tributaries of the Niger in such a way as markedly to reduce the intensity of biting at the dam site.

My own investigations were concerned not so much with the human aspect of the problem but with the relation of the control of *Simulium* by DDT to the development of fisheries. Fish farming depends upon the manipulation of a very complex biological system, and such systems can be grossly disturbed by the use of pesticides and herbicides. I hoped to see how far the oft-repeated use of soluble DDT might affect the biological system of the Niger and its tributaries. My colleagues and I in Liverpool have, with the help of Dr. R. A. E. Galley of "Shell" Agricultural Research, Woodstock, Oxford, evolved a method of selectivity controlling *Simulium* which has proved successful in temperate streams, in that no other creatures in the freshwater community constituting the food chain leading to fish have so far been affected (Kershaw *et al.*, 1965). I hoped to find out whether conditions near Shagunu were such that similar methods might be used.

It became quite clear that our methods of sampling streams and rivers to give reasonable information on the population dynamics of the aquatic forms of *Simulium* were inadequate. We found the larvae of *S. damnosum* in the River Swashi near the village, together with six other species, and in two small streams, nicknamed "The Grotto" which drains a swamp just below the laboratories at Shagunu, and "The Cascades", a fast-running stream running over boulders and entering the Niger some 3 miles south of Shagunu. In these last two places, we found *S. damnosum* and eight other species. The populations of these several species varied enormously. *S. damnosum* might be preponderant on one patch of grass and absent from another nearby. The catches of each species varied from day to day. The river might be flowing at 2 ft/sec one day and be waist high, the next day it might be a raging torrent and 20 ft deep. Sampling methods involving the use of polythene tapes placed in the water to provide a resting site for larvae and pupae gave populations as statistically unpredictable as those found on grasses nearby. Tapes placed in deep water in the River Niger itself showed two species of *Simulium*.

How many of these small streams exist in the catchment area of the Niger, west towards the Dahomey border and north-east towards Sokoto, one cannot imagine. It was possible only to survey one or two of these streams properly, since some are inaccessible on foot. The "Cascades" stream was found by casual exploration by boat in conditions of some difficulty.

The methods of sampling we have developed in Britain over the past five years give, we believe, satisfactory results in small streams which are perhaps 5 or 6 yd wide and about 6 in. to 1 ft deep. However, two years' work in the River Lune, in North Lancashire, which is some 6 ft deep and perhaps 20 yd wide and is liable to floods, has shown that methods based on a terrestrial approach are inadequate. Experience in the Niger and its tributaries has shown that our methods are quantitatively meaningless where there are so many resting places for the larvae and pupae of *Simulium* and where there is such variability in flow and depth of the waters. Before we can hope to observe the natural fluctuations in the populations of the aquatic forms of *Simulium* and understand their significance, much more basic work will have to be done both in temperate streams where sophisticated apparatus and advice is to hand and also in the field in Nigeria. The same remarks can almost certainly be made about any other aquatic creatures living in these conditions, such as algae, creatures living in the benthos, the plankton and even the fish.

In these circumstances it is idle to speculate at present about the effect of DDT in the Niger system or to make any intelligent statement about its effect upon fisheries.

REFERENCE

Kershaw, W. E., Williams, T. R., Frost, S. and Hynes, H. B. N. (1965). *Nature, Lond.* **208**, 199.

Man-made Lakes and Population Resettlement in Africa

T. SCUDDER

California Institute of Technology, Pasadena, California, U.S.A.

One of the results of the creation of large man-made lakes in Africa is the relocation of a substantial number of people, varying from some 50 000 Tonga in the case of Kariba to approximately 120 000 Nubians in connection with the Aswan High Dam Scheme. In Ghana, over 70 000 people (belonging to a number of distinct ethnic groups) are involved, or roughly 1% of the national population. A multi-ethnic population is also involved in Nigeria's Kainji Project with an estimated 50 000 people to be resettled by the end of 1968. As part of an integrated lake basin development plan, relocation on such a scale offers an exceptional opportunity for inducing rapid social and economic change. With proper timing and planning, new environments with new ground rules can be created in carefully selected relocation areas. Through experimentation both before and after resettlement, new production and extension techniques can be developed to increase per capita income without depleting soil fertility and other local resources. Subsequently they can be applied to previously settled areas where lack of similar controls is apt to make rural development a more difficult process. The opportunity here is indeed great. Its realization, however, requires that close attention be paid in the future to a number of important problems.

Of these the most important relates to timing. Irrespective of Government attitudes towards the local population and their development, in the Kariba, Volta and Aswan High Dam schemes little attention was paid to the resettlement process until after dam site preparations were initiated. At Kariba preparatory works began in 1955, with the main civil contracts awarded the following year. Of those people requiring resettlement, the majority lived in what was then Northern Rhodesia. Though the local District Commissioner and his immediate superiors were much concerned about the impact of resettlement on the Tonga by 1951 (when the consulting engineers chose Kariba as preferable to the Kafue site alternative), no positive action was taken on their request for an accurate ecological survey which could serve as the basis for the selection of resettlement areas and the intensification of agriculture following resettlement. Action was delayed until after the 1955 decision to proceed with the dam, and by then it was too late to undertake the type of detailed surveys required.

In Ghana the 1956 Report of the Preparatory Commission dealt with the "Effects of Inundation" in considerable detail. Soil suitability and other surveys, however, were not oriented toward the type of intensive settlement and agriculture which the Ghanaian Government subsequently decided to implement among those relocated. Though the Kaiser reappraisal of the Volta River Project was published in 1959 and preparatory works were initiated during 1961 with the main civil contract finalized that August, the head of the Resettlement Unit, with supporting staff, was not recruited until May 1962. As for the relevant soil suitability and social surveys, they were not initiated until after the commencement of dam construction. In Egypt, the general situation was similar. Preparatory works at Aswan were completed in 1955 with the first Russian loan negotiated in late 1958. The Social Survey which involved forty social workers over a 30-day period was not carried out until 1960, delaying the formulation of comprehensive plans almost until 1962.

Though it is not the purpose of this paper to analyse the factors involved in such a scheduling of activities that relate to resettlement, I am of the opinion that national and international planners underestimate the resource potential of a population undergoing resettlement and hence of the future lake basin itself. Initially, local government officials are also apt to underestimate the costs of resettlement in terms of capital, equipment and skilled personnel. Though inaccurate census data and lack of knowledge of where the future lake shore line will be no doubt contribute to such an underestimation, in large part I believe it relates to a lack of awareness of the difficulties involved in preparing new areas for large numbers of people and in physically relocating them and their belongings according to a rigid time-table.

Experience gained from the Kariba, Aswan High Dam and Volta schemes has shown conclusively in each case that there is too little time between the initiation and completion of dam construction to carry out and implement the minimal research needed for effective rehabilitation at the time of resettlement. Rather resettlement becomes a crash program to get the people physically moved before the river is sealed off. At that time the water level of the new lake can be expected to rise rapidly. At Kariba, for example, the water level rose approximately 50 ft during the first week, and was up 88 ft within a month. As for Volta, the river was sealed off on 19 May 1964 with the water rising over 20 ft by 1 June. Two months later it was 70 ft deep at the dam wall, with the depth exceeding

150 ft by the year-end. Under such circumstances resettlement must be completed on time or even earlier in case the contractors finish the dam construction ahead of schedule.

Because of the need for crash resettlement programs people are moved before the resettlement areas can support them. At Kariba (where no major attempt was made to transform the settlement pattern or agricultural economy of those relocated) it took the Tonga on both sides of the Lake approximately two years to clear and crop large enough acreages to meet their subsistence needs. Prior to that time, inadequate harvests forced them to rely on famine relief maize stock-piled by the Northern and Southern Rhodesian Governments. Famine relief was also necessary at Volta and was provided through the World Food Program. When I visited several Volta resettlement villages in February 1965 (which was a year after the establishment of some), I learned that the Government's ambitious agricultural development program was well underway in only one of the fifty-two planned communities. In a few others it was just starting, while in still others no formal program had been initiated. Though the Egyptian Government, like that of Ghana, saw resettlement as an opportunity to transform the social and economic organization of the people concerned, here too there had been insufficient time to prepare the new economic base. As a result in the major (Kom Ombo) resettlement area less than 10% of the land intended for irrigation was ready when the people were relocated. The remainder would be reclaimed during the two years following resettlement.

In both the Ghanaian and Egyptian cases, the opportunity to fit those relocated into a well-planned habitat from the start has been lost. Rather a demoralizing transition period must elapse before development requires the full participation of the people. During this, there is a definite risk that the more progressive segment of the population (whose energy will be needed at home once development gets under way) will seek work elsewhere while the less highly motivated become accustomed to living off government relief and/or funds remitted by wage-earning kin.

Aggravating the problem of inadequate time for well-planned resettlement and development are a number of other difficulties. The first of these relates to the very real strain that is placed on people undergoing compulsory resettlement, whether in Africa or elsewhere. This is especially the case, however, with major African hydro-electric schemes since dams are frequently sited, for topographical reasons, in rather isolated areas. Though the Nubian population displaced by the High Dam is an exception, frequently the populations involved have had relatively little contact with the outside world. Certainly this was the case at Kariba and Volta; it also would appear to be the case at Kainji on the Middle Niger.

As one result, those involved may not be able to comprehend the real
reason for their resettlement. The Tonga, for example, believed that their
movement had little to do with a dam miles down-river. Rather, many
believed that they were being relocated so that European settlers could
farm the fertile alluvia which had supported the Tonga in dense settlements for generations. This belief was strengthened rather than weakened
by bush clearing operations which were intended to prepare the lake
shore margin for the development of a gill net fisheries—planned with
Tonga interests very much in mind. Noting the similarity between clearing techniques and those used to prepare European holdings on the
Plateau, however, Tonga to whom I talked considered the real explana-
tion an insult to their intelligence! For how could a dam some 70 miles
down-river possibly flood areas several miles inland from the present
Zambezi channel? Here let me add that such a misunderstanding was not
merely a result of a colonial situation. In Ghana, local residents well up-
river from the dam site were incredulous that their own villages would
actually be flooded. Indeed, some suspicions were voiced that the move was
merely a Government device to get them out of the way so that their land
could be utilized in a different way (Amarteifio, undated).

Even if such misunderstandings are eliminated through improved
communication, those involved are bound to have many misgivings
about leaving an area with which they are psychologically and socially
identified. In the Tonga case, residents frequently pointed out that they
had lived near their present garden and villages sites for generations. Here
their ancestors were buried. Women, in particular, felt a close identifica-
tion with alluvial gardens (and their associated shelters) which had been
cultivated and inherited by members of their matrilineage for longer than
they could remember. Tied to other gardens as well as to shrines by
ancestral sanctions, neighbourhood ritual-leaders feared for their health
and that of their kin should they move elsewhere. Resettlement was also
seen as disrupting ties of kinship and friendship since Tonga who lived on
opposite banks of the Zambezi and frequently visited each other would
soon be separated by miles of lake and intervening bush. As for early
reactions to resettlement areas, they were influenced by their wilderness
aspects. With little involvement in resettlement planning, the Tonga
could hardly envisage how the area would look once the tsetse fly had
been pushed back and roads, water points, demonstration gardens,
health clinics and schools established. Even the early completion of a few
pilot facilities of the sort which the people themselves desired would have
alleviated anxieties as to Government intentions. They would have also
partially offset known deficiencies. For example, in discussing inland resettlement areas, the Tonga noted that they would no longer be able to

plant dry season crops along the banks of the Zambezi as the flood waters receded. Nor would they have access to certain wild fruits and famine foods which they associated only with riverine vegetation bordering (or lying immediately inland from) the Zambezi.

Though their nature varies, such genuine misgivings characterize all people undergoing resettlement and lead to increased anxiety. It is important that resettlement authorities be fully aware of this, and do everything in their power to widen channels of communication between themselves and the people. Though riots and disturbances against resettlement (such as occurred in Northern Rhodesia over Kariba and in the Sudan over the Aswan High Dam Scheme) may well be aggravated, for political purposes, by outside interests, their very occurrence is an indication of the extreme concern of the people involved. I doubt that it is accidental that such unfortunate incidents have been restricted to those situations in which the government planned to move people to distant areas with which they were unfamiliar. In Northern Rhodesia most Tonga were moved to areas with which they were familiar and which were only a few miles inland from their pre-resettlement homes. The riot which occurred in September 1958 was confined to those who had to be moved much farther (to the Lusitu area below the dam-site) because of land scarcity. Not only was this an area with which they were unfamiliar, but also one with an unfavorable reputation. Again because of land scarcity, those involved in the Sudanese disturbances were to be moved hundreds of miles south of Khashm el Girba on the Atbara River.

Yet another problem area relates to crises and irritants which arise during or immediately after resettlement. Though some difficulties are inevitable, since resettlement is, after all, a complicated process, some of those associated with the Kariba, Aswan and Volta schemes were a result of poor planning; itself a product of insufficient time and knowledge. Those that I plan to use as examples relate primarily to livestock, health, and housing. Perhaps because they did not realize their importance in the lives of the people, both the Egyptian and Ghanaian authorities expected those undergoing relocation to dispose of their sheep and goats. In the Egyptian case this was because of disease control and the government's awareness that there would be nothing to feed small stock in the Kom Ombo area for months to come. In the Ghanaian case no facilities had been prepared in the new towns for livestock. Regardless of the reason most people refused to follow the government directive (those who did sell their stock found that prices had dropped and hence hardly received a fair return). Though the Egyptian Government gave in, many stock subsequently died in quarantine at Aswan, while a significant proportion of the survivors died at Kom Ombo from starvation. In the Volta area, people merely brought their stock into the new towns, where I saw them wandering about unpenned, a source of annoyance to both government and settlers. Such situations are unnecessary. Inevitably they make those involved unhappy; at worst they increase the settler's resentment against relocation and government and create an environment unfavorable to cooperation.

Turning to Kariba, the earliest resettlement on a large scale was carried out by the Southern Rhodesian Authorities in 1956. Soon stories were coming across the river to the Northern Rhodesian Tonga (who had yet to be moved) that large numbers of people were dying of disease in the resettlement areas. Furthermore, settlers were said to be terrified by elephant and other big game in previously unoccupied land, while their stock were dying from sleeping sickness. As a result, the stories continued, some people had fled their new homes and were attempting to return to the Zambezi. Though one must, of course, question the accuracy of such stories, the important point is that the people believed them and hence were themselves less willing than ever to undergo resettlement.

Though I have inadequate information on what actually did happen on the Southern Rhodesian side, it may be significant that the highest mortality rates in Northern Rhodesia were reported in those areas with which the people were least familiar. Of 1 600 Tonga who were moved from the Valley floor to the Siagatuba area on the adjacent Plateau during 1958, forty-one children died during the first 3 months of 1959 (because the land was also hard to cultivate and livestock lost condition, these people were subsequently allowed to move elsewhere). As for the 6 000 Tonga who were moved some 100 miles down-river to the Lusitu basin, up to 100 people (mostly children) died during the months immediately following resettlement, with a majority of the deaths attributed to bacillary dysentery. A year later fifty-three women and children died of "an acute condition of sudden onset and high and rapid mortality" (Gadd et al., 1962). These deaths were concentrated in about eight villages one of which lost approximately 10% of its population.

Though the cause of this Lusitu condition remains unknown, a number of factors appear to be involved including a wild vegetable poison whose toxicity may well have been accentuated by certain states of mind. The timing of the deaths coincided with the annual stress period which was aggravated by resettlement. Though famine relief maize was stock-piled nearby, it is likely that the Tonga turned to this only as a last resort since they were expected to pay for such grain with funds received in compensation for resettlement. Rather than do this women and children followed their age-old practice of scouring the bush for edible wild food plants which at that season consist mainly of tubers. Quite possibly one of these was highly toxic but was eaten because it resembled closely an edible tuber which the people were accustomed to use in their former homes.

Among the Southern Rhodesian Tonga government policy was to provide a free monthly issue of maize and dried milk (along with less frequent issues of iodized salt) during those hunger months that occurred during the first two years after resettlement. Leaving aside the separate problem of compensation (for none was given in Southern Rhodesia), I consider this approach more realistic than that used in Northern Rhodesia where milk and protein were provided only after serious medical problems arose. Since the health of children is apt to suffer where it is the responsibility of the head of the household to purchase proper foods with his own limited financial resources, and because resistance to illness may well be lowered as a result of resettlement, the distribution of famine relief to each family should be the responsibility of the Resettlement Authority until the people have regained their self-sufficiency.

Where government is largely responsible for the creation of new towns, housing also may be a source of settler complaint during the early years of resettlement. Though the Egyptian government provided Nubian settlers with expensive and well-designed two- to four-room houses according to household size, these structures were built in a monotonous series of parallel rows with each row containing houses with the same number of rooms. While this procedure may well be more economical, it adversely effects the settlers since it breaks up larger residential units. Hence an old woman who is dependent on help from her married daughter's household prior to relocation, is apt to find herself living apart from her daughter in Kom Ombo. Though of a different nature, settlers connected with the Volta Scheme also had a number of legitimate complaints over housing. Still other complaints related to water supply interruptions and flies and mosquitoes breeding in septic tanks, irritants which taken together doubtless have considerable impact on morale.

Looking toward the future, many of the difficulties that have plagued past resettlement schemes can be anticipated and their impact minimized through appropriate planning and precautionary measures. Concerning the latter, it should be assumed, in the absence of evidence to the contrary, that a population's resistance to illness is lowered because of the very real stress accompanying resettlement and because of sudden changes in food consumption. Certainly the higher population densities which are frequently associated with resettlement increase the risk, for example, of epidemics of measles, chickenpox and bacillary dysentery. Their impact on parasite loads and tuberculosis should also be carefully evaluated especially among people who are unaccustomed to modern methods of sanitation and concepts of preventive medicine. It should also be assumed that additional medical and other problems will probably occur when it is necessary to move people to distant areas with which they are unfamiliar.

Basically what is needed is a more sophisticated approach to population resettlement. While in general I have been much impressed with the caliber and dedication of government civil servants responsible for implementing population relocation, the fact remains that they have virtually no access to international capital and expertise. This is in complete contrast to the design and implementation of major hydro-electric schemes whose feasibility is carefully researched into by reputable firms of consulting engineers and the international financing agencies, and whose construction is handled by leading civil contractors. To a lesser extent the same can be said of the evaluation of medical problems connected with the creation of man-made lakes and of the assessment of fisheries potential, since leading consultants usually are requested to visit the areas concerned and to prepare statements. In connection with resettlement, however, the formulation and execution of policy is entirely in the hands of government employees who may or may not have had previous resettlement experience. Though the Egyptian and Ghanaian Government at least involved high-ranking civil servants in the resettlement process, at Kariba resettlement was dealt with primarily on the provincial level. Nigerian policy seems to be following similar lines since resettlement is considered the responsibility of Northern Nigeria.

An obvious reason why the international financing agencies have not been involved in resettlement to date relates to the fact that they have not been asked to provide funds for resettlement purposes. Instead these are provided entirely from local currency. Though I am uncertain why this is so, it may well be that governments consider the relocation of their own nationals strictly a domestic matter. Regardless of the reason, however, failure to profit from other experiences with resettlement and to utilize international knowledge in connection with survey and resettlement execution is hardly in the national interest or the interests of the settlers themselves. For one thing the magnitude of resettlement is apt to be underestimated with insufficient funds provided from the start. This in turn leads to a small, over-worked staff and reduces the scope of essential surveys and hence the provision of detailed information which can be used for development following resettlement.

In years to come, I believe that resettlement and development connected with the creation of large-scale man-made lakes will continue to be carried out on a poorly timed, trial and error basis until certain basic policy changes are made; changes which view dams not just as a means for power generation and flood control, but rather as a means for an integrated river basin development program designed to raise the standard of living of the total population involved, both urban and rural. The very real problem of timing can be reduced if the necessary fisheries, hydrological, ecological, social and other surveys are included within the original feasibility studies. Though these are apt to continue over a number of years prior to site selection and the initiation of dam construction (following which a rigid schedule is essential), their scope is much too narrow. Though expansion would increase costs, these are hardly major in terms of subsequent benefits to both the people and the nation. On the basis of the Kariba experience, for example, within five years Lake Kainji should be able to support up to 2 000 fishermen with their families at a relatively high standard of living—provided the lake basin is prepared for gill net fisheries through the completion of adequate bush clearing. The Volta potential is even higher and would probably support (at a comparable level) twice the number of household heads that will eventually be employed at the Tema Aluminum Smelter, although again more extensive bush clearing is essential.

Turning to trial-and-error aspects of resettlement, these can be offset through an ability to profit from experience gained with resettlement in other countries both through the exchange of information and through the employment of those with relevant experience. Such experience should relate to the carrying out of rapid ecological and social surveys, the actual resettlement process, and the planning and implementation of development following resettlement. Needless to say, planning should take into consideration the opinions of the people for whom the plans are intended. It should also be based on an accurate assessment of the nature of both local natural and human resources. Concerning the latter, the strengths of human populations can be built into development projects while weaknesses can be offset from the start by the provision of whatever extension, credit, marketing and other facilities are considered necessary. At the same time research organizations, like the Nigerian Institute of Social and Economic Research, should be encouraged to make longitudinal studies of populations before, during and after resettlement. In the long run, such studies are bound to pay dividends by increasing the ability of planners to maximize the very real opportunities offered by population relocation, opportunities which to date have only been partially exploited.

ACKNOWLEDGEMENTS

Material for this paper was collected during two periods of field work in the Kariba Lake Basin (1956–57 and 1962–63) sponsored by the Rhodes-Livingstone Institute, Lusaka (now the Institute for Social Research,

108   T. SCUDDER

University of Zambia), a year's research in Egypt (1961–62) followed
by two brief visits (1963 and 1964) sponsored by the Nubian Project
of American University in Cairo's Social Research Center and a visit
to the Volta and Kainji Dam Projects in 1965 under the sponsorship
of the Africa Committee of the National Academy of Sciences National
Research Council.

I am indebted to my colleague, Dr. Elizabeth Colson, for the use of her
field notes on the Tonga inhabitants of the Kariba Lake Basin and for her
comments on a draft of this paper. I have also profited from conversations
with Dr. Frederick L. Dunn and with many individuals actively involved
in African resettlement (including, especially, E. A. K. Kalitsi, G. W.
Amarteifio and A. Smith).

Amarteifio, G. W. (undated). "Questions asked by the Villagers." A mimeo-
    graphed list compiled by the Volta Resettlement Liaison Officer.
Gadd, K. G., Nixon, L. C., Taube, E. and Webster, M. H. (1962). The Lusitu
    tragedy. *Cent. Afr. J. Med.* Suppl. 8, 495.

Discussion

WORTHINGTON: Scudder's work on the Tonga tends to suggest that when
people are moved there is a period of fluidity for a short time until their reactions gel into a new form. If so, then this adds to the urgency of preparations
in advance for fishery schools, etc.

SCUDDER: I agree. This period of "culture shock" is a period of fluidity.
Studies on refugees have shown that people may not be able to develop projects on their own initiative at this time but are susceptible to well-thought-
out ideas from outside. They accept the power that moved them (in this case
Government) as superior, so there is less chance that they will resist new
ideas. But, if two or three years go by, they settle into their old ways and may
react against new things. So the opportunity may be lost if there is a two- or
three-year delay between resettlement and the introduction of new ideas.

JOERIS: Experience at Kariba has shown that if the local people can see
results they pick up new ideas immediately. The local fishermen are rapidly
improving their catches and increasing their income, and we hope that they
will spend at least part of their increased income on new and better boats and
nets. This, however, may take some time. Possibly a sociologist could help
these people. They are rapidly learning of the pleasures of life that money can
buy from the newly arriving gamblers and professional female companions.

A small but increasing number of fishermen are making excellent progress
toward becoming full-time successful fishermen and many more are moving in
the right direction. The markets for fish products are developing rapidly
throughout Rhodesia and Zambia.

Archaeological Salvage in Man-made Lakes
(Lake Volta, Ghana)

O. DAVIES

Volta Basin Research Project, University of Ghana, Accra, Ghana

With the construction of the High Dam at Aswan, Egypt and the Sudan were able to make an international appeal for the rescue of their monuments, and to mobilize many foreign teams to help them record and rescue the archaeological sites which were due to be flooded. This was partly because they were first in the field, and their appeal had novelty and could attract workers and funds; also because Ancient Egypt has a great reputation, so foreign nations would realize that something important was being destroyed and would be enthusiastic to save it. Moreover, some monuments like the temple at Philae had been partly flooded by the earlier low dam, and stood as an indication of what more would be lost.

The problem above Aswan was further simplified because the Nile flows through desert, where ancient buildings and artifacts seldom are buried and can be easily surveyed. It has thus been the aim in the Nile valley salvage to record and excavate everything.

At Lake Kariba little attempt was made by the government of the Central African Federation to carry out archaeological salvage. No great effort was made to arouse interest in England, and it was apparently considered that there was little worth salvaging in the Zambezi valley. Dr. Bond and Dr. Clark undertook an extended survey of the Zambezi terraces and their archaeological content as part of the regular museum field-work at Bulawayo and Livingstone.

The building of the dam at Akosombo and the imminent creation of the Volta Lake led to a considerable effort to record and salve what was possible. A certain amount had previously been known about sites in the valley, but the inaccessibility of large parts of it had made exploration extremely difficult. There was little chance of obtaining international help, and even in the U.S.A. appeals for aid met with no sympathy. No team was prepared to come out on its own finances to work in the valley. But the Ghana government generously made considerable sums available so that it has been possible to supplement the author's work, mainly on survey, by the appointment of two research fellows to excavate those sites which seemed of importance.

It has not been possible to cover the whole floodable area. The lower part of the lake was extremely inaccessible, especially the west bank, and long stretches could not be reached even on foot. Moreover, though the lake hardly extends into the forest, the whole lake-area is in bush-savanna with high grass, where sites are extremely difficult to detect without erosion; and where there are no inhabitants, erosion does not normally occur. However, such surveying as it has been possible to carry out in the valleys of the Afram and the Volta up to 7° 30′ N. suggests that there are very few sites on the northern edge of the forest, probably because vegetation was very thick. From the confluence of the River Asukawkaw, up the Volta, the Oti and smaller tributaries, a great deal has been recorded.

The work has fallen into two parts, a survey of all the sites that can be found, and excavation where it seemed promising. The survey has covered the Volta terraces and their contained Palaeolithic material, with the examination of a certain number of peats formed in ancient lagoons in an early Holocene valley much wider than the present river; and some medieval and many early modern village-sites, the latter apparently dating mainly from the sixteenth and seventeenth centuries, since when it appears that people moved away from the rivers owing to the spread of riverine diseases, of which the most formidable was perhaps onchocerciasis. Where there was a good sequence of river-terraces, traverses have been taken. From peats samples have been taken for radio-carbon and palynological investigation. Stone implements and pottery have been collected wherever found. The number of sites recorded in the whole floodable area is approximately as follows:

Palaeolithic	70
Peat-sites (usually with hardly any archaeological material)	10
Mesoneolithic	121
Early Iron Age	14
Early Modern	116

Attention has been given to two other areas in Ghana likely to be flooded shortly. A good deal of preliminary survey has been carried out on Lake Bui on the Black Volta, and a start is being made this August on surveying the area of Lake Pwalagu on the White Volta.

In 1963–64 excavations were carried out at twelve sites on Lake Volta, one or two Mesoneolithic, two early Iron Age, and the rest medium sized villages of the early Modern period. The need for speed made it impossible to carry out more extensive tests to establish dates and stratification. There seem seldom to have been remains of structures, which would require the clearance of wider areas and so much time. In 1964–65 some attention was paid to smaller sites, but effort was especially concentrated on two large sites of particular importance: Bui to be flooded not by Lake Volta but by another dam further upstream, and Kitare on the Oti. The former was an important river-crossing; a long stratification and remains of a good many houses have been found. The latter was a huge triple-ringed enclosure with further subsidiary fortifications; only the lower part of it is due to be flooded, so it was above all necessary to make a complete plan and to examine the ramparts and gates which would go beneath the lake. In 1965–66 it is planned to examine another large town-site, at Buipe, and a number of high mounds which are almost certainly the remains of wooden towers.

In conclusion, I would offer a little advice based on the experience in Lake Volta:

(1) Complete archaeological clearance is impossible in heavily vegetated areas, and surveyors must be prepared to work largely on foot.

(2) Travel by boat is unsatisfactory, because it is difficult to land in gallery forest and one can see little of the banks from the water.

(3) Adequate time is essential, and the archaeological work should begin before even the dam starts to be built. We were a year late starting on Lake Volta, and so could do very little in the lower reaches.

(4) One surveyor can keep ahead of as many as four excavation-parties. He must be someone of wide experience, who can deal with Quaternary geology and Palaeolithic sites as well as fairly recent materials.

(5) There must be frequent liaison with base-headquarters, as excavators often need fresh supplies. It would be very useful for a lorry to visit each excavation fairly frequently for supplies and orders. Radiotelephonic communication with all field-parties would be extremely useful if it could be arranged.

General Discussion

R. JACKSON: The dialogue between scientist and engineer has, this afternoon, been extended to politicians and administrators. One must, when
considering these projects, contrast the ease of carrying them out in a developed country, such as Australia, where the Snowy River scheme is run by
an almost perfect administration, with the difficulties of carrying them out in
a developing country, where the sheer weight of immediate, day-to-day,
problems of the country explains some of the delays.

In both cases, however, there are often delays between the germ of the
idea and carrying out the scheme. Thus the idea of the Snowy River scheme in
Australia dates back to 1886, although the scheme was not tackled until 1949;
the Bakhra Nangal scheme in the Punjab dates back to 1907, but was only
tackled in 1947, and the Volta scheme conceived in 1915 was not tackled until
1961.

It has been suggested by some that planning for the Volta was inadequate,
but ten years ago the administration opened the door to scientists and every
piece of information on the Volta scheme and its effects was put together in the
comprehensive Report of the Preparatory Commission (1956). The report
indicated that the scheme would be viable, but then came a most difficult
phase, a hiatus while international finance was sought for the project. Factors
such as the state of the world aluminium market and East/West politics
affected decisions, and it was five years before construction started in 1961.
During this hiatus the scientific problems got into the background. Then
when the project started it was extremely difficult to get the administrators
to go back to the earlier reports. The resettlement problem, for example,
involved nearly ten years work, but there was then a break of several years
with a lack of momentum, when a crash programme became inevitable.

Similarly, in the Mekong complex in South-east Asia where there are at
present about forty survey teams dealing with the same kind of problems,
there is the threat of a hiatus while finance is sought, and during this time
there is the danger of a drop in the momentum of the scientific work.

The main justification for the Volta scheme was to get Ghana away from
dependence on a single crop, cocoa (and this has become particularly urgent in
view of the fall in the world price of cocoa). But whether the scheme would
come into being at all depended on the world price of aluminium. All estimates
had to be considered with this in mind, for if the price of power exceeded a
certain level the aluminium could not be produced economically and there
would be no project. The clearance of all the bush desirable for fisheries, for
example, was just not possible if Ghana was going to get aluminium onto
world markets at competitive prices. An arbitrary figure had to be allowed
for resettlement; if the Government wanted to do more, then Government had
to bear the cost. I should here pay tribute to Impregilo, the Italian contractors
who have already built the Kariba and Volta dams and who are now building
the Kainji Dam; they are really building modern pyramids in Africa. The end

result of their work is that Volta should provide some of the cheapest power in Africa.

The dendritic shape of Volta, criticized by some this morning, is really a great advantage, enabling a flow of protein to be carried into parts of the country where it would not otherwise penetrate, and providing new opportunities for inland transport.

The United Nations Special Fund is already involved with the research on Lake Kariba, and has received applications for help with the research planned for the Kainji and Nasser lakes. These are for action during the "during" phase of construction; as new projects come up it is hoped that research can be started well before construction is completed.

The mere fact that this symposium has been held should instil into governments the need for research. This symposium will be invaluable to administrators of such schemes if it brings out the time factors involved, the need to start the research early enough, and the danger of losing momentum during the hiatus period while finance is sought.

GWYNN: We are interested in Kainji. I would like to ask Dr. Scudder if the Niger Dams Authority are becoming aware of the difficulties that they are up against and whether he can suggest any solution, such as the appointment of a reservoir engineer? The Niger country has a very ancient and efficient system of government by Emirs with real authority, who can help in introducing new systems. Did the Tonga have the advantage of any such system?

I would also like to know what is meant by reservoir clearance. Cutting off and burning vegetation or rooting out? Engineers are not politicians and economists and have to convince these others. So if only limited resources are available, is it better to cut down the bush roughly, or clear a small area completely?

P. B. N. JACKSON: It is necessary to clear the ground and stump out if trawls are to be used, but for gill nets this is not so urgent and even waist-high stumps are permissible. But regeneration presents problems. At Kariba clearing was done one year and heavy regeneration took place the next year before the lake rose, so a billiard ball bottom is impossible anyway. The best way is to bulldoze the bush into windrows and burn it.

DOUGLAS: Kariba experience of primary productivity suggests that the *Aufwuchs* is far more important than the plankton from the point of view of fish production. Submerged trees offer large areas for high algal growth, and if there are browsers among the fish, would these then increase productivity? Is anyone working on this aspect in other schemes?

WHITE: At Kainji, Eaton of Bristol has been more concerned with the bottom and epiphytic flora than with plankton.

R. JACKSON: Summing up, it is clear that in any developing country there is need for a strong focal administrative point in government to deal with all the questions that must arise both at the policy and technical levels in analysing any multi-purpose project. Furthermore, problems tend to arise as projects progress; for example Mekong studies are now in their eighth year and the inflow of research is still going on. One must hope that a Mekong Authority will evolve when the present Vietnam troubles have been settled. The United Nations Special Fund is interested in preinvestment in all areas where there is reasonable likelihood that the particular project will, in fact, be brought to life.

The Natural History of Man-made Lakes in the Temperate Zone

Lakes in Dutch Reclamation Schemes

K. F. VAAS

Hydrobiological Institute, Yerseke, The Netherlands

As long as the Netherlands have been inhabited by man, land reclamation has been practised as one of the primary necessities of existence. However, the first major artificial lake was created when the Zuider Zee was closed by a dam in 1932. Moreover, this was the first time that agricultural, socio-economic and biological planning and research accompanied the activities of the technicians. Formerly a shallow basin of the North Sea, this was closed by a dam of about 25 km. The area of the basin amounted to 3 500 km². Along the borders a number of new polders were created and in the centre a new lake, known as Ijsselmeer, was formed, measuring 3 000 km². Near the dam the depth is 8 m, in the southern part 5 m. The dam was provided with locks and from the landside the River Ijssel brought in fresh water from the Rhine. Therefore it was possible to make the lake entirely fresh between May 1932, when the dam was finished and the minimal salinity was still 5·56‰ Cl', and 1937, when a fairly constant level of 0·16‰ Cl' was reached on the landside and 0·5‰ near the locks.

Changes in flora and fauna were studied by a large team of biologists and their results were summarized by Redeke (1922, 1936) and de Beaufort (1954). Some of their findings will be briefly mentioned.

As the silt, brought in by the rivers, was no longer carried out to sea by the tides, the bottom of the lake was levelled and visibility in the water decreased. The photosynthetic layer is at present about 2 m deep, with maximum photosynthesis at 1 m. However, phosphates and nitrates seem to be the factors limiting production, as phosphates are nearly totally consumed at the end of the spring bloom of phytoplankton. The city of Amsterdam drains its sewage into the lake at the rate of about 100 000 m³ per day. In the south-western part of the former Zuider Zee a rich fauna of Foraminifera, Nematoda, worms and molluscs lived on this sewage. Fortunately another fauna of Oligochaeta and Nematoda is now able to deal with the purification of this sewage just as efficiently. In the southern, brackish part of the former Zuider Zee a rare crab was found, *Rhithropanopeus harrisi tridentatus*. During the years when the salinity was decreasing this crab greatly enlarged its territory and was found throughout the entire Ijsselmeer, even penetrating into the neighbouring, slightly brackish, inland waters of the northern provinces. Towards the end of the period it began to decline and ultimately disappeared from the lake, still persisting, however, in the inland waters. In the year 1935, in the middle of the transition period to fresh water, the adults of a midge of the *Tendipes* group caused a minor calamity by emerging in enormous clouds. Motor traffic over the dyke was impossible for some time. The reason for this outburst was that the fish fauna, many representatives of which formerly lived on the bottom-dwelling midge larvae, was not yet in equilibrium. Herrings and anchovies, entering the Zuider Zee to spawn, and eels, had been blocked as soon as the dyke was finished. Cod and flat-fishes disappeared gradually. However, special measures were taken to facilitate immigration of elvers via the locks. The smelt increased in numbers, as did the freshwater species, ruff, pike-perch and some others. These were previously restricted to the mouth of the River Ijssel and now invaded the whole lake. It is mainly the ruff which holds the midge larvae in check. Without the introduction of any new species, a smaller volume of water now yields a larger crop of fish, viz. 20 instead of 12 million kg per year.

From a socio-economic point of view, two ideas lie behind the damming of this water. Firstly to push the sea water back as far as possible and deny the sea admittance to the centre of the country, and secondly to make fertile land available for the increasing population. When the dyke was finished and the first polders drained, many problems had to be solved, viz. agricultural problems, such as how to turn a soil previously covered by saline water into arable land, and sociological problems, such as the creation of entire new villages and village communities. Some of the fishermen, finding themselves suddenly without their habitual occupation, had to be trained for other trades and allotted indemnities.

However, with the damming of the Zuider Zee Dutch engineers did not consider their task finished. Realizing that the soil of the Netherlands is sinking—or rather tilting—at a rate of 1 cm in 100 years, and for this reason the sea is always encroaching on the land and increasing the salinity of the sea-arms and river mouths, they are constantly looking for new objectives, where the age-long defence against the sea can be turned into a frontal attack. The important sea-traffic of the country needs bigger harbours, but every one of these gives the sea a better opportunity to invade the inland waters. These waters are needed for irrigation of crops and for the ever-increasing demand for drinking water. The main source of fresh water is the River Rhine and the heavy industries of Germany, together with the salt mines of the Elzas, see to it that—at least during dry summers—the water of the Rhine can hardly be called fresh. Salinities of 230 mg/l of chloride are no exception in those periods. The oxygen content of the Rhine varies from 79% saturation to 29%. For the Meuse similar figures are much more favourable, but this river discharges only 10% of the amount of the Rhine.

In 1950 another sea-arm, with a surface of 800 ha (hectares) was dammed, viz. the Brielle Meuse, closed by a dam at Oostvoorne on the sea side and by the Botlek Dam on the land side, separating this artificial lake from the newly enlarged harbour of Rotterdam. The lake is constantly flushed by water from the rivers Meuse and Rhine but, owing to considerable seepage through the dam, its salinity still amounts to 0·75‰ Cl. Immediately after the closure the amount of seepage water was so large that it exceeded the total content of the lake in a year. Later on seepage decreased owing to infiltration of fresh water into the soil. The water is biologically characterized by a heavy bloom of *Aphanizomenon flos-aquae* var. *Klebahnii*, exceeding 50 million cells per litre in number.

Next came the closure of the Braakman in 1951–52. In the Middle Ages a shallow extension of the Western Scheldt, running in a north/south direction, almost cut the province of Zeeuws Vlaanderen into an eastern and western part. From then on, until the 17th century, this water was greatly enlarged by various storms. Then man began to make dykes and polders, reducing the area of the water to its present shape prior to damming in 1951. The result of the construction of the dam across the mouth was that now a dyke of 2·5 km holds the Western Scheldt in check, while formerly a V-shaped dyke of 27·5 km was needed to do this. Along the shallow shores various new polders could be constructed, adding 900 ha fertile soil and 400 ha sand to the territories of the Netherlands. As the depth of water amounted to a mere 12 m over a very limited area and the rest was very shallow, it was not difficult to make the water fresh.

At present another fairly large reclamation work is in progress in the north. A bight of the Waddensea, known as Lauwers Sea, is being shut off; the dyke is almost finished. The reasons for carrying out this work are: (1) better protection against the sea for the low-lying polders; (2) better control of the drainage; (3) land reclamation. When finished a central lake of 2 250 ha will be surrounded by 7 000 ha of land. The lake itself will be an attractive centre for recreation.

However, the above-mentioned projects must only be regarded as an introduction to the major effort in the field of man-made lakes at present in progress in the south-west of the Netherlands, in the deltaic area of the rivers Rhine, Meuse and Scheldt. These operations became known as the "Delta Plan" (see Fig. 1).

As a result of the extremely severe storm flood of 1 February 1953, about 130 000 ha in these areas were flooded and 1 835 people lost their

lives, while about 110 000 had to be evacuated. It was a disaster such as
the country had never before witnessed. Although years ago various
plans had been considered aimed at shortening the coastline, none had
been carried out. But directly after the disaster the Dutch Parliament
decided that most of the estuarine openings should be closed, the only

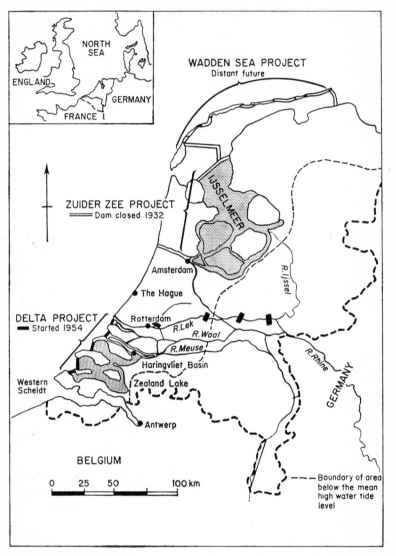

Fig. 1. Map of the Netherlands showing the completed Delta Plan and Frisian Islands
Plan.

ones to remain open being the entrance to the harbour of Rotterdam and the Western Scheldt, the entrance to Antwerp. The construction of the closing-dams will result in a shortening of the coast line by 700 km and the sea will be pushed back, thus creating higher security and reducing the dangers of seepage. Large areas of salt and brackish water will ultimately be filled by river water from the Rhine and the Meuse, which will become available for irrigation, to serve industry, and for the population as a source of drinking water. New and better roads over the dams will change a mainly agrarian area into one where industry can be founded, and water sports and recreation will flourish.

However, the flourishing oyster- and mussel-culture in the Eastern Scheldt will totally disappear.

To give an idea of the magnitude of this work, suffice it to say that the area of the Eastern Scheldt behind the future dam will be about 1 000 km^2, the dam itself about 9 km long, and, at some places, 20 m deep. The tidal difference in the mouth of the Eastern Scheldt is about 3 m and a millard m^3 of water flows in at every flood. The total work is planned to be carried out in 25 years, while the costs of the whole operation are estimated at 70–90 million guilders (some £7–9 million) annually for 25 years. The last dam will be finished by 1980.

The naturalist will be struck immediately by the biological consequences of this gigantic operation. In all estuaries and sea-arms tidal movements will cease abruptly when the dykes are completed. It is intended to flush the thus created basins as quickly as possible with the water of the rivers Rhine and Meuse, and turn them into freshwater lakes. Land reclamation is not an important aim in this project. What minimum salinity will be ultimately reached is a difficult question, in view of the enormous discharge of brackish water from the polders and in view of the fact that the Eastern Scheldt contains some large basins where the depth is more than 30–40 m. As was the case when the Zuider Zee was turned into the freshwater lake Ijsselmeer, enormous changes will take place in flora and fauna. However, in contrast with the Zuider Zee, where a single body of water was involved, this area includes a number of waters of very different character.

The Eastern Scheldt does not receive any important discharge of river water and is therefore characterized by a relatively constant salinity throughout its length. This fact, combined with higher summer temperatures and sheltered situation, is responsible for the establishment of a rich marine flora and fauna, containing several species here growing at their northernmost limit of distribution.

On the other hand, the mouths of the Rhine and Meuse, called Hollands Diep and Haringvliet, form a typical estuary with a marked longitudinal

E*

salinity gradient as well as vertical salinity stratification in the centre.

As the hydrographical situation differs widely in the above-mentioned waters, the present flora and fauna will differ as well, and we can expect different reactions when the dykes are finished and the water begins to lose its salinity.

In view of the important scientific results of biological investigations carried out during the Zuider Zee–Ijsselmeer transition, the Royal Netherlands Academy of Sciences decided to create a laboratory at Yerseke, on the shores of the Eastern Scheldt, and to give it the task of describing and analysing the changes to be expected. From 1959 this laboratory has been working in the area, studying littoral and benthic fauna, fishes, plankton, halophytic shore vegetation and hydrography. Since that year the staff has grown to comprise at the moment seven biologists and a chemist, together with supporting personnel. About thirty publications have appeared in international and Dutch scientific periodicals, and annual reports are published in English every year in the *Netherlands Journal of Sea Research*.

It is evident that changes in biota can only be investigated if the situation before the changes occur is known, so the initial phase of the work of the laboratory must have the character of an inventory. However, as far as possible, inventory work is carried out from an ecological point of view. The work of den Hartog (1963, 1964a, b) on Talitridae, Gammaridae, flatworms and molluscs, and the work of Beeftink (1962) on halophytic vegetation form examples of this approach.

However, there is a single objective where changes have already taken place. When in April 1961 the dam through the sea-arm known as Veerse Gat was finished, a new lake was created called Lake Veere. On the eastern side of the lake a dam with locks had been constructed one year before. The first dam sealed off the lake completely from the sea, the eastern dam, near the village of Kats, forms a limited connexion with the Eastern Scheldt. Let me conclude this paper with some results of the biological and hydrographical investigations carried out by our laboratory on this lake. Further details can be found in an article by Bakker (1964).

At present the surface of Lake Veere is about 20 km² and its maximal water content amount to 87 million m³. The shape is elongated with its long axis running in a east-west direction for about 28 km. There is a gully in the centre between 6 and 12 m deep, but there are about half a dozen narrow deep pits of 20–25 m. For agricultural purposes, viz. the draining of the neighbouring polders, two water levels are maintained, a summer level of 0 NAP (Dutch Ordnance level) and a winter level 70 cm lower. This means that every year in April water from the Eastern Scheldt is added and this influx amounts to about 15% of the total content of the lake, because along the stream gully extensive areas of very shallow water are found. In autumn the same amount is discharged.

At the time of closure the salinity was about the same as in the Eastern Scheldt and for the first year fluctuated between 15 and 18‰ Cl. From then on three influences came into play: in the first place evaporation, in the second place rain and drainage from the polders. If these two had been the only ones, the salinity would have decreased continuously. However, the annual influx of water from the Eastern Scheldt and discharge of mixed water means an annual injection of salt, and therefore the salinity soon reached a level of 10–11‰ Cl′ and with slight fluctuations stays there. In the deep pits near the sluices of Kats the Eastern Scheldt water is more or less trapped and here salinity at the bottom is higher. Also in the deeper strata of some other pits, the salinity is higher owing to seepage.

The severe winter of 1962–63 covered the entire lake with an ice layer 50 cm thick, and the temperature of the saline water dropped to values of -1 to $-1\frac{1}{2}°C$ at all depths. At the same time the differences in salinity between the surface and bottom increased, since the wind could not now stir the water under the ice. Differences between 10‰ Cl′ at the top and 14‰ at a depth of 15 m were found. When the ice disappeared in spring and the temperature of the upper layers rose, extremely marked temperature stratification was noted in the deeper parts. Sometimes a homogeneous layer, 10–15 m thick, with a temperature of 12–15°C, was found over a clear-cut thermocline of a few metres, followed by a cold bottom layer, with temperatures ranging from 4° to 0°C. In autumn homothermy was restored, but in early winter cases of stable, inverse temperature stratification could be found, with, for example, water of 2° on top and 6°C at the bottom. The higher salinity at the bottom made the density of the warmer water exceed that of the colder water over it.

Drastic changes of flora and fauna were also observed. From the very day that the dyke was finished all bottom-dwelling algae and molluscs in the shore zone, no longer inundated at high tide, began to die. Later on, when the salinity had fallen, the former luxurious vegetation of Fucaceae was changed into an algal flora dominated by *Enteromorpha* spp. However, in this case the decrease in salinity could not be the cause of the change, as Fucaceae grow in the Baltic at lower salinities. Several sandbars, formerly inundated every day, became permanently dry, and after some time a vegetation of *Senecio vulgaris*, *Salix* and *Epilobium* spp. began to develop on them, with an outer fringe of halophytes. Before the closure a rich flora of centric diatoms flourished in the water, composed of the same species as the coastal sea water and that of the Eastern Scheldt. With the decrease in salinity most of them disappeared.

However, concomitant with the change in salinity, another change took place. The city of Middelburg used to drain its sewage into the former sea-arm, at a rate of 3 000 m³ per day. It was intended to meet the new situation with a pipe line from Middelburg to the Western Scheldt in the south, but this line was finished a year too late, so for a year the closed Lake Veere received a lot of sewage. As a result phosphate values rose . temporarily from 5 μg atom/litre to between 20 and 40 in the western part. The constant discharge of water from the polders also added phosphate to the water. At present the phosphate level is about 15μg atom/ litre. This eutrophication resulted in an outburst of small flagellates, reaching 10 million cells per ml.

Typical brackish organisms such as *Acartia tonsa*, *Synchaeta littoralis* and *Neomysis integer* developed strongly. The rich plankton caused the benthos to flourish too. Although the number of species decreased, the surviving ones, species of *Corophium*, *Polydora*, *Nereis* and various lamellibranchs, developed strongly. The fish fauna also reacted to the abundant supply of food. Although the number of species decreased as a result of the barred influx from the sea, those species able to propagate in the lake—eel-pout and two species of goby—increased very much in numbers, and those species formerly visiting the lake "in transit" showed very rapid growth. Among the latter group the plaice merits attention.

From their birthplaces in the English Channel and the North Sea, the plaice enter our coastal waters and sea-arms and as they grow older swim out to sea again to spawn. So a sample of plaice from the Eastern Scheldt consists of fish of zero and 1 year of age, with a few older ones. These plaice were "trapped" in Lake Veere when it was closed. There is a limited possibility of escape for them, via the locks at Kats, but so far it cannot be proved that they use it. The results of monthly investigations go to show that large numbers of these trapped plaice of the 1961 year class are living here, notably in the western part of the lake. Their growth is rapid and their guts crammed with food. In two successive years we have seen their gonads ripen and eggs and sperm being discharged, but neither larvae or fry could ever be found among the numerous larvae of other fishes. However, young plaice swim in via the locks and this influx might counterbalance the large catches of plaice made by professional fishermen, who operate about 200 fykenets.

Even at this stage, when the most difficult parts of the "Delta Plan" have not yet started, still further plans are being made, and perhaps after twenty or thirty years you will be told about the "Wadden Sea plan", connecting the islands Texel, Vlieland, Terschelling, Ameland, Schiermonnikoog and Rottum with the mainland of the northern provinces of the Netherlands and draining part of the Wadden Sea.

REFERENCES

Bakker, C. (1964). Planktonuntersuchungen in einem Holländischen Meeresarm vor und nach der Abdeichung. *Helgoländer wiss. Meeresunters*, **10**, 456–472.

Beaufort, L. F. de (1954). "Veranderingen in de Flora en Fauna van de Zuiderzee na de afsluiting in 1932." Den Helder.

Beeftink, W. G. (1962). Conspectus of the phanerogamic salt plant communities in the Netherlands. *Biol. Jaarb. (Dodonaea)* **30**, 325–362.

Hartog, C. den (1963). The amphipods of the deltaic region of the rivers Rhine, Meuse and Scheldt in relation to the hydrography of the area. I. Introduction and hydrography. II. The Talitridae. *Neth. J. Sea Res.* **2**, 29–67.

Hartog, C. den (1964a). The amphipods of the deltaic region of the rivers Rhine, Meuse and Scheldt in relation to the hydrography of the area. III. Gammaridae. *Neth. J. Sea Res.* **2**, 407–457.

Hartog, C. den (1964b). Proseriate flatworms from the deltaic area of the rivers Rhine, Meuse and Scheldt. I. *Proc. K. ned. Akad. Wet.* C, **67**, 10–34.

Lingsma, J. S. (1964). "Holland and the Delta Plan". Rotterdam.

Redeke, H. C. (1922). "Flora and Fauna der Zuiderzee." Den Helder.

Redeke, H. C. (1936). "Flora and Fauna der Zuiderzee." Supplement. Den Helder. 176 + 82 pp.

Vaas, K. F. (1963). Annual report of the Delta Division of the Hydrobiological Institute of the Royal Netherlands Academy of Sciences for the years 1960 and 1961. *Neth. J. Sea Res.* **2**, 68–76.

Vaas, K. F. (1964). Annual Report of the Delta Division of the Hydrobiological Institute of the Royal Netherlands Academy of Sciences for the year 1962. *Neth. J. Sea Res.* **2**, 284–292.

Vaas, K. F. (1965). Annual Report of the Delta Division of the Hydrobiological Institute of the Royal Netherlands Academy of Sciences for the year 1963. *Neth. J. Sea Res.* **2**, 605–614.

Discussion

PENTELOW: Can water of 10–11 p.p.m. chloride content be used for agricultural purposes?

VAAS: No.

YONGE: Are there going to be permanent estuarine conditions behind the barrages with the high chloride content of Rhine water—conditions in which fish might feed and grow, if not breed?

VAAS: When all the dams are finished the intention is to flush out with Rhine water. The Rhine is of low salinity when the water is high, and can be used to flush the system of reservoirs. The dams are due to be finished in 1980, and engineers think that by 1985 the salinity will be like that of the Zuider Zee at present. The Zuider Zee in a smaller area of water now produces more fish than before enclosure.

YONGE: So you expect a completely freshwater system eventually?

VAAS: We hope so, but I have doubts because the Eastern Scheldt has some deeper spots. It depends on the skill of the engineers in flushing them with fresh water. The water coming in is already mixed, so there will be a gradual system of freshening. Wind turbulence and seiches may influence the mixing. We hope it will not be necessary to use artificial means, though bubbling screens will be used if necessary; these are used to counteract seepage through locks.

LUND: You mention the loss of *Fucus* when the salinity fell to nil, *Enteromorpha* replacing it, but see from the Baltic no reason for this on salinity grounds, so why has the *Fucus* gone?

VAAS: We noticed *Fucus* had gone and thought at first that it was the salinity drop. Concomitant with the salinity decrease was an increase in eutrophication and a decrease in light penetration. So far we have only tackled the descriptive side and no experiments have yet been made. We hope to have an algologist by November 1965 for such studies.

NEWTON: Has any *Fucus serranoides* come in?

VAAS: There is none in the lake.

CORLETT: You mention plaice in the Eastern Scheldt. What are the bottom deposits like and has there been any change in these?

VAAS: As eutrophication proceeded large blooms of flagellates had effects on the benthos. At present the bottom, which is sand and in some places mud and peat, has huge numbers of *Corophium*, *Nereis* worms and small molluscs. Plaice guts are crammed full; there are so many worms on the bottom that plaice do not bother with worms on the hook. The anglers are not satisfied but the plaice are!

The Biological Implications of the Proposed Barrages across Morecambe Bay and the Solway Firth

H. C. GILSON

Freshwater Biological Association, Ambleside, Westmorland, England

Changes on the scale of an estuary barrage in a system as complex as a large, shallow arm of the sea with its mudflats, sandbanks and channels, would seem likely to be both far-reaching and complicated—so complicated perhaps as to be well nigh unpredictable. But while such an impression is probably right in matters of detail, reflection reveals that the change from being covered with sea water or brackish water part of the time and saturated with water although exposed to the air for the rest, to being covered with fresh water all the time, is really less drastic, biologically speaking, than the flooding of dry land or even the change from forest to cultivation. One is therefore encouraged to think that the attempt to predict some of the results in general terms may be worth while. In such cases the biologist usually turns to precedent and experience. Unfortunately the number of Morecambe Bays and Solway Firths that have been dammed in the past is small, but the conversion of the Zuider Zee into the Ijsselmeer has some relevance.

It is perhaps useful to begin by dividing the biological consequences of building a barrage into those that affect the usefulness of the barrage when built, and those that stem directly from the resultant changes in the fauna and flora. Examples of the first group are the biological properties of the impounded water, or effects on the amenities of the area; examples of the second are effects on the fish and fisheries of all sorts on both sides of the dam. But since effects of all types, some good and some bad, may result from a particular change in the biota, it is more convenient to the biologist to consider the problems from the viewpoint of the properties of the environment and the types of organism that live or are likely to live there.

Assuming that one of the most important objects of building an estuarine barrage (Figs. 1 and 2) is to make the impounded fresh water available for human use, domestic or industrial, one of the most practically significant biological properties of the water will be its productivity, because what lives in it affects the treatment required to render the water

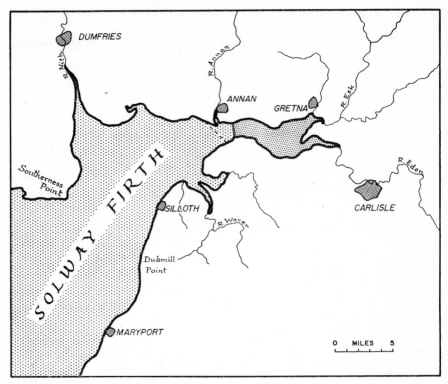

Fig. 1. Map of the Solway Firth showing the barrage lines proposed by Drew (1964; two alternative positions).

suitable for most purposes. In the long run productivity will be mainly determined outside the reservoir by the nature of the inflowing water, but the basic potential so derived may be modified by such properties as temperature and turbidity determined in the reservoir, and by the more mobile elements of the fauna such as birds. For an initial transitional period, the environment will be further modified by interstitial sea water held temporarily in the bottom deposits. Thus to begin with the high sulphate content of the deposits will favour the growth of sulphate-reducing bacteria and the formation of an evil-smelling mud of the type common in estuaries. Amounts of sea salt in the mud and overlying water will fall progressively as the salt is leached out, at a rate depending largely on rainfall and catchment area. Dutch experience suggests that this transitional phase would probably not last more than three or four years.

What the rivers bring in depends partly on the geology of their basins and partly on what is put into them along their courses. With the

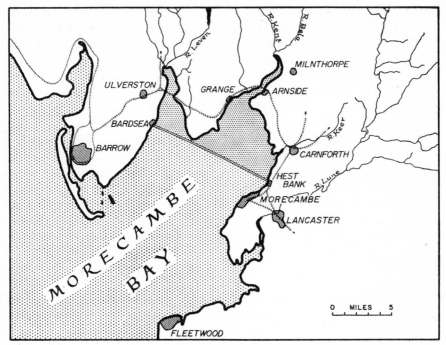

Fig. 2. Map of Morecambe Bay showing the barrage line proposed by Leeming (1964).

exception of those industrial wastes that contain toxic substances of an inorganic nature, which are in most cases small in volume, what man adds as sewage, as industrial wastes, or as added fertilizers leached from agricultural land, tends to increase the potential productivity of the water. I say "potential" because effluents containing much oxidizable organic matter (poorly treated sewage or milk wastes, for example) some- times produce conditions in a river in which this potential cannot be immediately realized. It should be noted that it is the enduring inorganic additions, rather than the evanescent organic ones, which matter in this context. Most rivers then, contain near their mouths water capable of supporting abundant growths of algae and other plants. It follows that the water impounded behind an estuary barrage will be likely to produce enough algae to pose some treatment problems to the water engineer. But this is not a serious difficulty; the methods of treatment are well known from experience with many waters of riverine origin, such as forms, for example, a large part of London's supply.

I have already mentioned a modifying factor of some importance in controlling the growth of algae and rooted plants—turbidity. In most estuaries, suspended solids maintained in suspension by turbulent tidal streams, severely limit the penetration of light and so the growth of both plankton and attached vegetation. I know of no measurements of this property in Morecambe Bay, but work done by the Atomic Energy Authority's staff from Chapel Cross (Perkins *et al.*, 1964) indicates that some settlement takes place even during the periods of slack water at high and low tide. The exclusion of the tide by an estuary barrage can therefore be expected to allow the water to clarify by settlement with a corresponding increase in the depth of the zone in which active plant growth is possible. The matter is not, however, quite as simple as this. Although it has been shown that in most estuaries the muddy deposits come from seaward rather than from the land, some suspended matter is brought down by rivers, and this tends to flocculate and precipitate in the presence of sea water. In a reservoir it might tend to remain in suspension, but the amount is probably small (I have no figures) in the rivers entering Morecambe Bay, larger in the Solway. In water kept fresh by the dam, although tidal turbulence would be excluded, wind-induced turbulence might suffice to keep some of the finer material in suspension.

This leads to the consideration of one property of the reservoir, which may be important here, and which is within limits under the engineer's control. This is its depth—not the maximum depth, but the average depth of much of its shallower parts, which would form a large proportion of the whole in Morecambe Bay or the Solway Firth. The shallower the water, the more easily will its bottom deposits be stirred by the wind, but also in water not less than 3 or 4 ft deep the better will be the conditions for the growth of rooted plants, which themselves tend to prevent stirring of the bottom. The balance of advantage here is not altogether easy to evaluate. More rooted plants will tend to leave less "chemical fertility", to use a convenient expression, for plankton algae, thereby easing filtration problems. On the other hand water plants can produce smells and tastes —the Characeae, which are rather common in fresh waters near the sea, are particularly objectionable in this respect. They can also yield embarrassing quantities of loose debris, especially after a severe autumn gale. Areas not more than about 10 ft deep are likely to become covered with rooted plants.

The abolition of tidal changes in level together with the substitution of fresh for salt water, will make conditions more favourable for marginal vegetation. In bays and inlets which are sheltered and where silt has accumulated, extensive growth of the common reed (*Phragmites communis*) is to be expected, so that some of the margins of the reservoir might come to resemble the Norfolk Broads. But the reed is intolerant of exposure to wave action and therefore likely to be limited to places where the waves have a limited fetch. In more exposed parts and along stony shores, the less complete vegetation cover would probably include the reed grass (*Phalaris arundinacea*) in many places, as it does along the shore of Lough Neagh. These changes in marginal vegetation are not likely to raise any particular problems, provided that water intakes are suitably screened to exclude weed torn loose by storms. On the contrary, they might well come to be regarded as an improvement to the amenities, and large areas of reeds could well become sanctuaries for rare birds such as the bittern.

Abundant vegetation of whatever kind is likely to support a rich invertebrate fauna less varied than the marine and estuarine fauna it replaces but probably more plentiful. Insects, Mollusca and Crustacea can be expected to form a large part of this, and one of the most numerous families would probably be the chironomid midges. Many cases are known of reservoirs where these insects are produced in numbers large enough for the adult midges, which do not bite, to be a considerable nuisance on account of the dense clouds of them that form when the adults are emerging. These have been known to impede road traffic, annoy the housewife by settling on washing on the line, and appear in embarrassing numbers at lighted windows. They thus represent a potential threat to local amenities. Experience suggests however that this is a problem which only becomes serious in environments that are ecologically unbalanced, as a new reservoir is bound to be for an initial period after its completion. Thus chironomids became a nuisance in the Ijsselmeer until it was colonized by fish in numbers sufficient to control the midge larvae (Vaas, p. 120).

Invertebrates other than midges do not seem likely to cause problems or difficulties. They are fairly easily filtered out of water supplies. On the other hand, the abundant invertebrates of all kinds would provide a rich supply of food for fish, several species of which can be expected to do well in a barrage reservoir. We must however consider fish with different habits somewhat separately.

The larger of the rivers flowing into Morecambe Bay and the Solway are well known for their brown trout, sea trout and salmon, and some of them, the River Eden for example, also contain several species of coarse fish. Let us leave aside for the moment the migratory fish, since they pose some special problems. There seems no reason to expect that the building of a barrage would have any particular effect on the upstream populations of resident fish, except in so far as interference with the migratory species might reduce competition. Thus, if fewer salmon and sea trout came up, there would presumably be more food and more space left in the upper reaches for the brown trout. On the other hand, the upper parts of the rivers would provide a source from which the barrage reservoir could be rapidly colonized. The brown trout's known habit of travelling about a good deal makes one suggest that it might be the first to colonize a new reservoir, particularly as this species is fairly tolerant of salt water. Moreover it is quite likely that some of the sea trout (zoologically the same species but with different habits) might stop on finding good feeding in the reservoir, and adopt behaviour somewhat parallel to the slob trout's habit of hanging about in estuaries instead of going on out to sea. I am therefore inclined to predict good trout fishing in the reservoir, at least for the first few years. Something similar has often been observed in inland impoundments. As time passed, however, and the salt leached out, the weed would increase and the reservoir would become much more the sort of place coarse fish usually inhabit. This leads me to think that after three or four good years the trout fishery would gradually decline over the next five-to-ten years and be replaced by perch, roach, rudd, and pike, and perhaps bream and tench if they were introduced. Under these circumstances excellent coarse fishing, perhaps especially for pike, might continue.

Of the migratory fish, as elvers would easily find a way in, eels would almost certainly thrive as they do in Lough Neagh. Provided that water was discharged into the sea during late summer and autumn floods (August to November approximately), suitable arrangements for trapping silver eels on their way out to sea should not be difficult to make, and a profitable fishery might result.

But salmon and sea trout present more difficult problems, partly because of the need to provide both for the upstream movement of adult fish, and for the downward movement of smolts to the sea in the spring. If sufficient water were discharged through the dam at all, or nearly all, times, it would be possible to provide fish-passes up which adult fish could go reasonably easily, and in which the annual run could be counted. But this would not be done without some experiment on design. What is more difficult to forecast is how easy it would be to devise an arrangement that attracted in-coming fish in the sea to the outfall of the pass. The fact that there are rivers on the rocky west coast of Scotland (the Gruinard, Little Gruinard and Polly are examples), which run steeply into the sea with a minimum of estuary but yet have runs of salmon and sea trout, suggests that this problem should not be insoluble. Smolts, on the other hand, might well have difficulty in finding their way across the reservoir to a comparatively small sea outlet. It should be possible, although some cost would be involved, to trap them near the river mouths and transport them to sea. This would have the advantage that they could then be acclimatized by a period in brackish water such as they normally encounter in an estuary and would miss by going directly over a spillway into the sea. Such a procedure would also provide an unprecedented and much to be desired opportunity to study the relation between the smolt run and the run of adult fish in a particular river.

A possible alternative approach to the salmonid problem would be to write off the fisheries and compensate owners of fishing rights. In the Solway, where there are extensive fisheries both in the Firth and in the rivers, this would be a formidable operation. In Morecambe Bay the cost would be less. In either case political and amenity considerations might render such a proposal unacceptable.

Of the effects on the marine element of the estuarine fauna there is not a great deal to be said. Clearly all the marine and estuarine animals would disappear from the area above the barrage. This would mean the disappearance of such things as shrimp and cockle fisheries from that area. The lines so far proposed for barrages (Figs. 1 and 2) would leave a certain amount of more or less similar ground below. If, as it might, the barrage made this area more accessible, the final effect on such fisheries might be small. If, on the other hand, the barrage by altering tidal streams caused considerable changes in the configuration of the bottom in the seaward parts of the estuary, the effects on the inshore marine fauna might be considerable but unpredictable without detailed information on the physical changes.

To sum up, then, there are a number of biological considerations which should be kept very much in the minds of the engineers during the design stages of a project of this sort. If due account is taken of these facts there would seem to be no insuperable problems or very large additions to costs. On the contrary considerable advantages from the research point of view might be realized in relation to migratory fish.

REFERENCES

Drew, R. L. (1964). "Solway". Annan (published privately).
Leeming, E. L. (1964). "Morecambe Bay Barrage". Manchester (published privately).
Perkins, E. J., Bailey, M. and Williams, B. R. H. (1964). The biology of the Solway Firth in relation to the movement and accumulation of radioactive materials. VI. General hydrography, with an appendix on meteorological observations. U.K.A.E.A. Production Group Report No. 604 (CC).

Discussion

ATKINSON-WILLES: How much accretion of silt can be expected in the estuary once the dam is built?

GILSON: This is an engineer's problem that I cannot answer, but there is a lot of sand and mud there. Work in the Solway suggests that most of this comes from the seaward, not the landward, side; moreover, the rivers are fairly clear, so that the rate of the addition of silt may be comparatively small, although there is a good deal of movable silt in the bay and alterations in tidal streams will affect this. Probably models would be necessary to answer this question. It will also depend on the level at which the water is kept; also if weeds grow over the bottom these will tend to stabilize the silt.

WORTHINGTON: You mention oscillations in level for supply; but I thought the idea was for the whole flow of the rivers to go in and the amount taken out would always be less than the total flow of the affluent rivers, so there would always be water over the spillway and the level would be fairly constant. Is it possible to increase the yield by overdrawing in dry weather? Then there would be no flow over the spillway in dry weather, though migratory fish may need some water over it the whole time.

GILSON: There will certainly be some variation in level, but not a large one —not as large as in Thirlmere.

RYDZ: Mr. Gilson mentions rooted growth in shallow water behind the barrages. If reeds cover a considerable area and are left high and dry for up to twelve months say once in ten years, would one expect water troubles from the decay of this vegetation?

GILSON: *Phragmites* is fairly tolerant of varying water level and of silt (but does not like wave action) so I doubt whether this would have much effect— but I am not a plant ecologist.

GIFKINS: I am concerned about the smolts being moved from fresh to salt water.

GILSON: There is no need to put them straight from fresh to salt water, one could acclimatize them.

GIFKINS: Can aquarium and pilot schemes give some answers? Are any planned?

GILSON: This I cannot answer, but the schemes' feasibility studies will take biological problems into account, though how this is to be done I do not know.

PENTELOW: I think that smolts would find their way through the More-cambe Bay lake if the barrage is built. For 10 000 years they have been finding their way through Loch Ness. Pike would make inroads on but would not stop the smolt migration—the pike population will be geared not to the smolts but to whatever they have to live on for the rest of the year when there is no smolt migration.

OLIVER: I disagree with Mr. Gilson's view that trout would give way to coarse fish in Morecambe Bay. I have had experience with a lake which formerly had many millions of coarse fish. These have been reduced to quite a manageable proportion by stocking very heavily with large trout. The trout is a predator but man is a greater predator. The trout get removed but the coarse fish get put back. Unless this is kept in balance the coarse fish will multiply. With proper management through stocking trout with the right age and right size, Morecambe Bay could probably become an excellent trout fishery. The age of the stocked fish is important as they do not rise to a fly after their third year.

GILSON: There is no real disagreement. I meant that it would change to a coarse fish water if nothing particular is done about it. No doubt it could remain trout water if it was properly managed; this would involve some expenditure, but some financial return is possible.

Hydro-electric Schemes in Scotland
Biological Problems and Effects on Salmonid Fisheries

K. A. PYEFINCH

Freshwater Fisheries Laboratory, Pitlochry, Scotland

Over the last twenty years, hydro-electric developments have taken place on a number of Scottish rivers and have had their effects on their biology. During this period a good deal of attention has been given to the problems which such developments create for the populations of migratory fish which are such a characteristic feature of many of these rivers. Not all the river systems have been affected and the degree of interference varies from one to another, but some idea of the effect can be gained from the generalization that, of the thirty-five fishery districts in which at least 3 000 salmon and sea trout were caught in 1963, nine have been affected by hydro-electric developments. It should be added that, judged on a catch basis, the biggest salmon rivers of Scotland have been less affected than those with rather more moderate catches, for of the seven fishery districts in which at least 30 000 salmon and sea trout were caught in 1963, only one carries a major hydro-electric scheme.

The principal theme of this paper will be to review the problems created, assess the effects produced, so far as these are known, and to describe the ways in which attempts are being made to minimize or eliminate any disadvantages which have appeared. Practically all the work that has been done in Scotland on the biological problems of hydro-electric schemes has been concerned with fisheries, as even the observations which have been made on other elements of the freshwater community (e.g. Campbell, 1957, 1963) have mainly been connected with the food supplies of the fish. As salmonids are the most important freshwater fish in Scotland, most of the studies made have been on salmonids and, within this family, on Atlantic salmon. Brown trout, with their less extensive migrations, have posed fewer problems and sea trout, though their migrations out of and into fresh water are comparable with those of salmon, have not received much attention, perhaps because they are chiefly abundant in the smaller river systems, which have fewer attractions for the hydro-electric engineer or in the lower reaches and tributaries of the larger river systems which, on the whole, have not so frequently been harnessed for power developments.

The development of a hydro-electric scheme on a river can affect it in several ways. First, it can affect the contour of the river. Instead of the naturally decreasing gradient from source to mouth, the river is modified, to a greater or lesser extent, to form a series of steps with the reservoirs or impoundments forming the treads of the stairway. The extreme development of this kind is seen in some of the Swedish salmon rivers, where virtually every available metre of head, from source to mouth, has been utilized. None of the Scottish rivers have reached this extreme condition though a river such as the Tummel, which originally flowed through a series of lochs which have now been converted into impoundments, is perhaps the nearest approach to conditions in Sweden.

Second, hydro-electric developments affect the regime of the river. Instead of the natural alternation of spate and drought conditions, flow is more uniform. The actual volume of water released downstream is usually negotiated between the hydro-electric authorities and the District Fishery Board concerned. Often, arrangements are made for the volume of compensation water to vary seasonally, e.g. on the River Meig in Ross-shire, one of the tributaries of the Conon River system, the compensation flow is 37 cusec from mid-March to mid-October but only 9 cusec for the remainder of each 12-month period. Sometimes, arrangements are made to release artificial spates at intervals during the spring and summer. These are intended to stimulate the upstream movement of adults, but their value in this connexion seems doubtful. Some observations on this point have been made at the trap below Meig Dam. Here the flow over the trap was increased from 37 cusec (the normal summer flow) to 121 cusec and then decreased again to 37 cusec. The changes in flow were made in stages, each stage lasting 12 h. No clear relationship was found between volume of flow and the number of salmon entering the trap and, in fact, observations suggested that increased flow from a burn just above the Meig trap, which followed heavy rain, was a greater inducement to fish movement (Pyefinch and Mills, 1963). The range of increase of flow that could be utilized in this experiment was limited but the results observed are similar to those found by others (e.g. Hayes, 1953).

When an obstruction is erected across a salmon river, provision is normally made, usually by means of a fish-pass or fish-lift, for upstream and downstream migration past the obstruction. In some cases, however, the construction of a fish-pass is impracticable or uneconomic and, under these circumstances, an attempt may be made to compensate for the loss of access to the spawning grounds by providing facilities for catching the adults, stripping them and rearing the progeny, sometimes to the fry stage and occasionally to the smolt stage. In some countries this practice has been used extensively; e.g. in Sweden the salmon stocks of many of the major salmon rivers, which have been almost entirely converted into a series of impoundments, are being maintained by a number of smolt rearing stations scattered up and down the country, but in Scotland fry or smolt rearing is only practised to a limited extent at present. One reason for this is that hydro-electric developments are not so extensive but there are also doubts about the "quality" of the smolts that can be reared under Scottish conditions as, judged on the basis of the numbers of adults which return from releases of hatchery-reared smolts, the latter are inferior to natural smolts.

All these considerations suggest that the development of a hydro-electric scheme on a river which contains migratory fish may produce disadvantageous effects but unfortunately it is not easy to assess the over-all extent of any effects produced. This arises because, in Scotland, there are virtually no records of the fish stocks of these rivers before the system was modified. In some cases records of angling catches are available but these are intrinsically very variable and, in any case, the relationship between catch and stock is unknown. The only hint of the effects of hydro-electric developments is that which is provided by the counts of ascending fish which are now made at a number of dams. Over the years immediately following the closure of the dam it may, perhaps, be assumed that the counts give some indication of the pre-closure runs so that these may be compared with those in later years, when any effects of the modifications may show themselves. Table I below gives the records at two

TABLE I

Upstream Runs of Salmon at Pitlochry and the Meig Trap

| Year | No. of fish ascending | |
	Pitlochry	Meig trap
1951	5 630	—
1952	5 790	—
1953	5 368	—
1954	5 357	—
1955	4 182	—
1956	3 555	—
1957	4 339	613
1958	3 513	256
1959	3 074	246
1960	3 930	220
1961	3 741	149
1962	3 998	231
1963	4 353	375
1964	4 ,522	479

sites, Pitlochry on the River Tummel, a tributary of the Tay system and the trap on the River Meig, a tributary of the Conon system. Pitlochry Dam was closed in 1950 and Meig Dam in 1956.

In both instances, there was a marked decline in the runs shortly after the dam had been closed but, over the past three or four years, there are some signs of an improved trend. This may have been produced by measures taken to improve the runs (e.g. fry planting in the upper reaches of the river, above the impoundment) but in both cases it should be remembered that the records refer to tributaries of a river system, so that the counts may be affected by differences in the distribution between the various tributaries of the river system. Such differences may well occur from year to year in river systems unaffected by hydro-electric developments, though detailed records to support this suggestion are not available.

The need to provide some means of passage for migratory fish at any obstruction has, of course, always been recognized but the particular difficulties associated with obstructions connected with hydro-electric schemes were not always realized immediately. Fish-passes have been provided at natural obstructions for many years but, under these circumstances, the main problem was to facilitate the upstream passage of the adults to the spawning grounds. At least on most Scottish rivers, downstream passage for the spent adults or for parr or smolts presented no serious problems, because the downstream migrants could pass over the obstruction if they failed to find the fish-pass, but this is not always the case at a dam built for a hydro-electric scheme. Under these conditions, one route downstream, that into the turbine intake and through the turbines, was potentially dangerous and so exit by this route was prevented by erecting screens across the turbine intakes, with mesh of a size which would prevent at least the smolts and larger parr from entering the intake. Thus the only exit for downstream migrants was the fish-pass or fish-lift built into the dam. This situation has a serious disadvantage. Though the only exit from the impoundment is the fish-pass, the main flow of water, at least when the turbines are running, is into the turbine intake. Thus the problem presented to the downstream migrant is to locate the entrance to the fish pass when the main flow of water is towards an exit which it cannot use. The solution to this problem which has been offered to the fish has been expressed, as it were, in human terms, namely, that if exit A, which is obvious, is blocked, then the migrant will search for, and eventually find, exit B which, although smaller, is open. It is by no means certain that the fish can solve the problem in this way. Its downstream migration may be guided by different responses to other stimuli and these responses may prevent the fish from solving the problem correctly. For example, current must be one important stimulus to downstream migrating fish and a number of observations suggest that the response of a salmonid fish moving downstream to an acceleration in the current is to head upstream. Thus a fish approaching a turbine intake may, at some stage, respond to the increasing current speed by turning and perhaps swimming upstream. Later, it may again turn downstream but if it again approaches the turbine intake, it is reasonable to suppose that the same sequence of events will occur again. Therefore, overall, the response of the fish is not necessarily to seek another outlet, but to be held in the impoundment as a result of its responses to the major stimuli of its environment.

This suggests that one effect of the interpolation of artificial obstructions of this kind will be to delay downstream migration. It is not easy to obtain direct evidence of the extent of this delay but there is evidence which suggests that delay is one of the causes of other disadvantageous effects which have been observed. In 1957 a census of upstream and downstream migrants was begun on two tributaries, the River Bran and the River Meig, of the Conon River system. Natural spawning was allowed to take place in the Meig, but no adult fish were allowed to pass into the Bran; this stream was stocked by planting unfed fry in the upper reaches. Counts of the smolts migrating from the Bran, made at a trap which lies below the impoundments on this river, showed that only a very small proportion (about 0.05%) of the fry planted subsequently appeared in the trap as migrating parr or smolts. An investigation was therefore started to try to discover the cause of this exceptionally heavy loss. This showed (Mills, 1964) that smolt production from the Bran itself was not unduly low for a rather unproductive Highland river; almost 3% of the fry planted reached the lower reaches of the Bran as migrating parr or smolts. The losses occurred as these migrants passed through the impoundments. The latter contained pike and brown trout which were found to be predators of the migrants and the latter were also, at certain points on the course, subject to predation by birds, chiefly goosanders. The losses may well, therefore, have been due to the interacting effects of delay and predation.

Even in the absence of predators, delay may have a serious effect on the number of migrants which reach the sea. There is evidence that the "migratory urge" in young salmonids may only last for a limited period. If the migrants are delayed as they move downstream, this "urge" may wane and migration will cease. Some observations made in the River Tummel may support this suggestion. For a number of years, members of staff at the Freshwater Fisheries Laboratory, Pitlochry, made observations on the migration of parr and smolts at various points on the Tummel system and in particular at two dams, Dunalastair and Clunie, which are situated about 10 miles apart, roughly at either end of Loch Tummel. The migrants caught at Dunalastair were marked before release. All the migrants passing Clunie Dam were inspected and it was found that, in successive years, only 13·4%, 28·7% and 20·7% of the fish marked at Dunalastair reached Clunie. Though a few of the remainder appeared the following year, most did not do so and here again delay, and perhaps predation, may have been the cause of the heavy loss.

One way out of the difficulties produced by the screened intakes to turbines would be to remove the screens and allow the migrants to pass downstream through the turbines. This procedure is not as alarming as it might sound as, in most hydro-electric turbines, the spaces within the machine are big enough to allow a fish of smolt size to pass through and the runner itself revolves comparatively slowly. So far, it has been the practice in Scotland to screen the intakes to turbines operating at heads of more than 100 ft. Tests have therefore been going on, for the last three or four years, to discover the effects of passing smolts, or trout of smolt size, through turbines operating at greater heads. These tests are not yet complete but present indications are that about 10–20% of the migrants may be damaged as they pass through turbines operating at heads of about 170 ft. Damage is greatest when the turbine is "running up", decreases markedly when the turbine comes on load and some further decrease occurs as the load on the turbine increases to about three-quarters maximum. From this level to full load there is some increase in the amount of damage. Though the proportion of fish damaged is significant and could be serious if the downstream migrants have to pass through several power stations on their way to the sea, these losses have to be considered in relation to the serious losses which may occur if the migrants are delayed *en route* downstream.

Another, and more radical, way of eliminating the difficulties caused by hydro-electric developments is to collect the downstream migrants at some suitable point above the dams and impoundments and transport them downstream to a point where they have an uninterrupted run to the sea. Physical conditions may prevent this being done in some instances, but where it can be applied it seems a useful way round the difficulty. An experiment on these lines has recently been started on the River Bran. Here arrangements were made to trap the migrating parr and smolts above the section of the river affected by impoundments and dams and transport them, by road, to a point below the lowermost dam. This experiment was started in 1963 so that there has already been an opportunity to assess the promise of this operation from the numbers of grilse recaptured last year. Weather conditions during the smolt run in 1963 hampered trap operations, but 649 migrants were transported and, for comparison, 240 parr and smolts were released just below the trap to make their own way downstream. Of the latter group, only 7·9% reached the trap below the impoundments and none have returned after a period in the sea, whereas all the transported fish survived their road journey and, so far, 2·8% have been recorded on return from the sea. This proportion, which may rise as more two-sea winter adults are caught this season, is almost a tenfold increase over the earlier returns from this river system.

Operations such as transportation of smolts are clearly temporary expedients rather than full solutions of the problem of guiding migrants down, or up, a river affected by hydro-electric developments. It is also clear that much more knowledge of the behaviour and physiology of salmon, at all stages in its life history, is needed for a full solution of this sort of problem. Progress here must inevitably be slow but the facilities and techniques are beginning to be available for thorough investigations within this field. Much work of this kind is in progress in North America, using Pacific salmon but, as the title of this paper specifically mentions Scotland, reference may, perhaps, be restricted to work going on in that country.

During the past four years, observations have been made on the responses of salmonids to passive displacement by water movements. These are part of an investigation of the factors in the environment which release an orientated movement in fish with the ultimate aim of discovering some means of guiding fish and so ensuring that their downstream passage is made as quickly and safely as possible. Studies are also in progress on the behaviour of salmonid fish at falls and obstructions. Stuart (1962) has published an account of the first stages in this investigation which indicates the way in which salmonids leap over obstructions. This work is of great interest biologically but it is also of considerable importance practically, since many of the findings can be applied to the design of fish-passes. During this investigation, some work was also done on downstream movement. This stemmed from the field observation that fish normally found no difficulty in moving out of a pool of natural profile, that is, one in which the deepest part was at the head or middle and where the depth decreased gradually towards the outflow, but found considerable difficulty in escaping from a pool in which there was deep water immediately upstream from the outflow. Laboratory experiments in which these pool types were simulated indicated that, if a sloping ramp was placed projecting upstream from the lower end of the second type of pool, the fish were able to pass downstream without difficulty. An impoundment for hydro-electric generation is, of course, a pool of the second type on a grand scale and Stuart's results suggest that the provision of inclined ramps leading to the fish-pass exits should facilitate the downstream movement of migrants. This device has yet to be tested on a full scale, but a pilot-scale test in an artificial outdoor channel has given very promising results.

One point should be emphasized in conclusion. This account of some of the difficulties created for migrating salmonids by the development of hydro-electric schemes may have given the impression that, in the design of such schemes, the engineer has given little attention to the problems of salmonid fisheries. This is far from being the case, much thought, effort and financial outlay has been expended in trying to devise means of safeguarding these valuable fisheries. The biologist, however, is only beginning to be able to answer the shrewd questions which these developments pose.

REFERENCES

The references listed below are mainly those of the reports which have been published on the topics discussed in this paper. Full details of some of the work have not yet been published but brief reports on these investigations may be found in the annual reports of the Department of Fisheries and Agriculture for Scotland ("Fisheries of Scotland"), particularly from 1959 onwards.

Campbell, R. N. (1957). The effect of flooding on the growth rate of brown trout in Loch Tummel. *Freshwat. Salm. Fish. Res.* No. 14, 7 pp.

Campbell, R. N. (1963). Some effects of impoundment on the environment and growth of brown trout (*Salmo trutta* L.) in Loch Garry (Inverness-shire). *Freshwat. Salm. Fish. Res.* No. 30, 27 pp.

Hayes, F. R. (1953). Artificial freshets and other factors controlling the ascent and population of Atlantic salmon in the LaHave River, Nova Scotia. *Bull. Fish. Res. Bd Can.* No. 99, 47 pp.

Mills, D. H. (1964). The ecology of the young stages of the Atlantic salmon in the River Bran, Ross-shire. *Freshwat. Salm. Fish. Res.* No. 32, 58 pp.

Pyefinch, K. A. and Mills, D. H. (1963). Observations on the movements of Atlantic salmon (*Salmo salar* L.) in the River Conon and the River Meig, Ross-shire. I. *Freshwat. Salm. Fish. Res.* No. 31, 24 pp.

Stuart, T. A. (1962). The leaping behaviour of salmon and trout at falls and obstructions. *Freshwat. Salm. Fish. Res.* No. 28, 46 pp.

Discussion

NOTE: When presenting his paper, Mr. Pyefinch mentioned other points connected with the effects of hydro-electric developments, including the use of louver screens for diverting downstream migrants and the value of using hill lochs as nursery grounds for young salmon.

HAMILTON: Have the louvers, in the colour photographs shown by Mr. Pyefinch, been tested at other water speeds?

PYEFINCH: No, the range of water speeds tested was limited. A major disadvantage of louver screens is that their efficiency decreases at low water speeds. It may be possible to overcome this by combining an electric screen and a louver screen.

SANDISON: Has any work been done on the colour of the louvers, or on moving louvers to compensate reduced efficiency in slow currents?

PYEFINCH: We have not tested louvers of different colours, nor discovered the effect of moving louvers. Work has been done in Canada on the effect of moving chains and other devices. Some of these gave promising results when tested on a pilot scale but proved less effective in full-scale tests.

CRAGG-HINE: Dr. Pyefinch mentions rearing salmon fry. Evans and Jones from the University of Liverpool have been carrying out experiments in planting fry in lakes in Snowdonia for some years now.

F

The Biology of Reservoirs in the U.S.S.R.

JULIAN RZOSKA

Freshwater Productivity Section, International Biological Programme,
and Sir John Cass College, London, England

This survey is based solely on the study of Russian literature, the author's practical experiences being with water reservoirs in the Sudan. In connexion with some other (zooplankton) work, twenty papers on the development of biological events in reservoirs have been selected out of a vast number, and their translation arranged; in addition, other Russian papers have been consulted, published mainly in the *Proceedings of the International Association of Limnology*. The complete list of references on which this survey is based is given in the Bibliography.

There must be many hundreds of reservoirs in the U.S.S.R., mainly of fluviatile origin, distributed over the whole of the Russian Eurasian subcontinent and over several climatic regions. It seems that most of these artificial water bodies have been constructed over the last forty years mainly for technological reasons within the framework of Russian planned economy. It is not evident that biologists have been consulted as to sites and constructions of the dams, but it is certain that a large body of biologists from universities and other institutions was mobilized to keep a watch on biological developments during, and often even before, the filling of the basins. Further, a rich older literature existed on many of the rivers involved before the advent of reservoirs. Great attention was paid to phytoplankton, zooplankton, benthos and micro-organisms; a flow of cross information was fostered by symposia and, with the importance of reservoirs as potential sources of food recognized, a special Institute for the Biology of Reservoirs was created at Borok. This publishes regularly Proceedings and a Bulletin. With the intensity of human interference and management of water resources rising all over the world, close attention must be paid to the vast experience of our Russian colleagues.

A study of even a selection of Russian references on reservoirs gives the impression of discernible phases in this work. There are a great number of fact-finding papers; some, because of the underlying emphasis on practical (fishery) results, contains prognoses of future developments. Some of these turned unfavourable and the investigation of causes led to attempts

149

to generalize and make the recommendations for remedial interference. The phase has now been reached when the existing observations allow for principles to be evolved for the classification and differential management of these water bodies.

The fact-finding phase dealt with effects of damming on individual rivers and detailed descriptions of developments in the phyto- and zooplankton, the benthic fauna and the fish stock during the first year of filling the reservoir. This is the phase of quick and drastic changes. The original stock of river organisms undergoes a severe selection and elimination according to adaptability to new and changing conditions normally connected with dams across a river. Phytoplankton changes from the usual scanty diatomaceous condition both in species and quantity; in some suitable reservoirs cyanophycean species begin to appear. The animal suspension carried by rivers, composed of some true plankton forms with a large admixture of adventitious (littoral and benthic) forms alters drastically by the dropping out of the latter, because of reduced currents, and regrouping in dominance and composition of the remaining plankton forms; rotifers still dominate the scene in the first stages but the crustacean element increases. Most drastic are the changes in the benthic fauna, where the rheophilic elements are quickly dying. After 9 months only fifty-six out of 150 river species survived in the Mozhaisk reservoir on the River Moskva. Previous shores, with a phytophilic fauna, are drowned and new terrains are inundated with the existing terrestrial fauna of earthworms and others persisting for some time. Sedimentation of the bottom of the reservoir is accelerated and slowly new colonizers, chironomids, move in; generally the biomass sinks. Fishes lose their former spawning grounds, especially those accustomed to rock–gravel conditions and those spawning in the previous shore vegetation.

In some reservoirs the inundation of considerable areas of terrestrial vegetation and arable land causes a passing eutrophication with an increase of bacterial decomposition and release of nutrients from the leaching soils. A passing increase of general productivity appears with even an increase of growth rate in fishes, which may feed on the drowned and dying terrestrial fauna. Changes are noticeable in chemistry and temperatures; stratification may appear in deeper parts, as may deoxygenation, though never as intense as described from tropical conditions.

The succession in the following second and third year already showed regional differences. Phytoplankton developed in southern, warmer reservoirs differently from that in northern regions. Cyanophycean water blooms appeared in alkaline regions; no mass developments took place in some northern reservoirs. Zooplankton decreased sharply in number of species, Crustacea began to exceed Rotifera in biomass though not always in numbers, longitudinal differentiation in quantity of zooplankton appeared towards the dam site. The benthic fauna again showed the biggest evolution. Of the original river fauna only mud associations survived; phytophilous elements, when present, began to colonize the new submerged grounds, if suitable. A most spectacular and frequent phenomenon was the extensive development of Tendipedidae especially in the new shore areas. The former river bed now enlarged and under deep water, was gradually covered by sediments, colonized by tubificids and chironomids. An increase of biomass was often noted. The fish fauna was still changing. After three years only forty-seven out of seventy river species were found in a Dnieper reservoir. In the lower Volga reservoirs, of forty-three original species all seven Caspian migrants dropped out and the remaining thirty-six species showed fluctuations.

At this stage the question of further changes emerged and the problem of biological stabilization. Attempts at forecasting were apparently required and made. As far as one can judge some assessments had to admit unfavourable developments. This must be expected; biological habitats are labile when interfered with and our knowledge of biological interrelations is not sufficient to make accurate predictions in many cases. The case of Lake Arpilich in Armenia is relevant. Previous to damming there was a thriving local carp fishery there based on rich water vegetation. This was drowned and never recovered. Though a rich zooplankton persisted, fishing diminished greatly and after eight years of existence the lake still did not show stabilization. Other cases concern the appearance of unwanted cyanophycean blooms, gaps in food chains, invasions by unwanted organisms like *Dreissena*, mass development of sponges especially in arid zone reservoirs, deficiencies in biomass of plankton and benthos to sustain a large crop of fish. In many cases stabilization of new biological set-ups took a longer time than anticipated.

But enough experience was accumulated to allow for some common outlines of reservoir development to be recognized and for principles of biological management of reservoirs to be advanced. A number of summarizing reviews appeared: e.g. Dzyuban (1959) on zooplankton, Mordukhay-Boltovsky (1961) on benthos, Kouznetsoff (1961) on microflora, and Zhadin (various papers, e.g. 1947, 1961) on general trends of development. Recognition of various trends of reservoir development encouraged attempts at classification of reservoirs (e.g. Melnikov, 1962). Some of the main results are given here.

Reservoirs on rivers differ from lakes by their asymmetry of depth distribution towards the dam, development of longitudinal differentiation, absence of sublittoral, changes in water level, throughflow with varying coefficient, more sedimentation. They develop differently in different climatic regions: in *size*, those in mountains usually being smaller than those in the plains; in *existence*, as their "lifespan" depends on erosion and sedimentation; in *purpose*, reflected in hydrological regime imposed by man; in *morphology*, which offers varied conditions for depth and relief; in *temperatures* with climatic region; in *nutrients*, with allochthonous inflow and environmental landscape.

A classification by Melnikov arranges reservoirs according to altitude (lowland, mountains) and according to river systems belonging to biogeographic regions. Further classificatory criteria employed are currents and throughflows, length of vegetative (summer) season, climatic regime. Kouznetsoff stresses chemical characters, changing north–south and, closely connected with these, development of microfloral processes; he regards the numerical relation of bacteria generally to the saprophytic bacteria as a good indicator of maturation processes of reservoirs.

Where reservoirs have been observed for longer periods, previous assumptions of quick stabilization had to be revised. In the Utchinsk reservoir on the Moska–Volga canal zooplankton became more or less stabilized only after ten years and then is still subject to annual fluctuations. Bottom faunas on the lower Volga reservoirs were still labile after eighteen to twenty-three years.

Two phenomena decide on long-term developments in reservoirs according to Zhadin (1947): firstly the supply of organic and mineral substances from inflows, and secondly the supply of organisms from previous stock, natural inflows, insect colonization, all of these supplies selected out by the power of adaptability.

Left to natural development, reservoirs would acquire their new stable biological regime very slowly. In many cases, e.g. in France, Japan and the U.S.S.R., there was a recognizable reduction of fish production. With the strong emphasis in Russia on terminal production of fish, further human interference has been recommended and carried out in numerous cases. Deficiencies in phytoplankton production are to be remedied by fertilization. The necessity for the introduction of "intermediate" food animals has called for acclimatization attempts of Caspian invertebrates (Mysidacea, Cumacea, snails etc.) into southern reservoirs. Artificial spawning grounds were to be created where natural ones were lacking, and the fish stock was to be reinforced by fry from adjacent hatcheries. The usually rich zooplankton of reservoirs, at present not exploited sufficiently, is to be cropped by the introduction of plankton-eating fishes.

It is evident that reservoirs are large-scale experiments and that this programme is still to be intensified. Already reservoirs have played a considerable role in changing the distribution of freshwater fauna in

Russia. The spread of northern species of lacustrine fauna (*Bythothrephes, Heterocope*) into southern Volga reservoirs, where conditions were thought to be unsuitable, is remarkable. On the other hand, the natural advance of Caspian species north previously so conspicuous has been handicapped in the case of some groups. Widespread introduction and acclimatization of Caspian species of invertebrates counteracts the artificial interruption of river systems by dams.

This very brief survey of a small part of Russian literature on man-made lakes cannot give a full account of the manifold work; for this more detailed reviews are necessary.

BIBLIOGRAPHY

(On which the above survey is based.)

Note on transliteration of the Russian alphabet. Apparently there is no universally accepted method and one name may be quoted as: Zhadin, Shadin, Schadin; this must create confusion. I have adopted the transliteration used by the National Lending Library for Science and Technology, Boston Spa, Yorkshire, England.

Papers marked * are translated by the above library and available at various prices from the library. Only the translated titles of these papers are given.

From *Zoologitcheski Zhurnal*

*Borutskii, E. V. (1949). Formation of the zooplankton of the Utchinskoe reservoir on the Moscow Canal. **28**(1), 71–78.

*Melnikov G. B. and Lubyanov, I. P. (1958). Formation of the zooplankton and bottom fauna of Simferopol reservoir in the Crimea. **37**(6), 820–831.

*Meshkova, T. M. (1960). Changes in the fauna of Lake Arpilich as a result of its conversion into a reservoir. **39**(11), 1597–1606.

*Ulomskii, S. N. (1959). Plankton formation in the Kama (Perm) reservoir. **38**(1), 3–14.

Zhadin, V. I. (1947). Principles of mass development of living organisms in reservoir. **26**, 5.

From *Trudi zonalnogo sovieshchania po tipologii . . . vodoemov youzhnoi zonyi S.S.S.R.* 1962

*Dzyuban, N. A. Reservoirs as zoogeographical factor. 105–110.

*Melnikov, G. B. The question of classification of reservoirs. 155–160.

*Ozhegova, V. E. Facts relating to the hydrobiological characteristics of the Kairak-Kumsk reservoir during the first year. 172–176.

*Tseeb, Y. Y. On certain regular features associated with the formation of the hydrobiological regime in the Kakhovsk reservoir. 204–210.

*Vyushkova, V. P. Zooplankton of the Volgagrad reservoir in the first year of its existence. 81–83.

From *Trudy VI Sovieshchanya po poblemam biologii vnitrennikh vod.* 1959

*Dzyuban, N. A. On the formation of zooplankton in reservoirs. 597–602.

*Grimalskii, V. D. Zooplankton of the Dniestr and its changes under conditions of the Dubosary reservoir. 365–370.

*Lokhanina, L. A. Preliminary data on the formation of zooplankton in the Gorkii reservoir. 340–346.

154   JULIAN RZOSKA

*Melnikov, G. B. The establishment of the biological regime of the Simferopol reservoir. 459–463.
*Romadina, E. S. A study of the zooplankton of the Volga river, using samples collected at the construction site, 1953–54. 347–351.
*Yaroshenko, M. F. and Naberezhnyi, A. I. Special features of the hydrobiological regime in Dubosary reservoir. 371–377.
From *Uchinskoe i Mozhaiskoe Vodokhranilishcha. Izdatielstvo Moskovskogo Universiteta* 1963
*Sokolova, N. Iu. The benthic fauna of the Mozhaisk reservoir during the first year of its existence. 355–374.
*Vilenkin, B. Y. Pelagic zooplankton of the Utchinsk reservoir. 213–225.
*Uspenskii, I. V. The zooplankton of the Mozhaisk reservoir in the first year of its existence. 375–387.
From *Verh. int. Verein. theor. angew. Limnol.* 15, 1961. (All in German.)
Kuznetsov, S. I. Hauptrichtungen in der Erforschung der Mikroflora der Wolgastauseen. 665–672.
Mordukhay-Boltovskoy, F. O. Die Entwicklung der Bodenfauna in den Stauseen der Wolga. 647–651.
Roll, J. W. and Zeeb, J. J. Der Stausee von Kachovka am Dnjepr. 636–639.
Shadin, W. J. Die Wirkung von Stauseen auf natürliche Gewässer. 792–805.
Sokolova, N. Die Entwicklung der Bodenfauna des Utcha-Wasserbeckens. 640–642.
From other sources
*Kozhevnikov, G. P. (1961). The Gorkii reservoir. *Izv. Gos. Nauchn-Issled. Inst. Ozern. i Rechn. Rybn. Khoz.* 50, 51–61.
Luferova, L. A. (1963). The formation of zooplankton in the Gorkii reservoir. *Tr. Inst. Biol. Vodokhranilishch. Akad. Nauk. SSSR.* 6(9), 130–142.

Discussion

EWER: Are there any indications that the time of stabilization is faster in the south than the north, and of the speeds at which reservoirs stabilize?

RZOSKA: I cannot say.

BECKMAN: I will try to answer Professor Ewer's question whether high or low latitude reservoirs stabilize more rapidly. The Russian I. I. Lapitsky notes three phases in reservoir stabilization: (1) a sudden increase in standing crop; (2) a depression which lasts some time; (3) a gradual increase in productivity. He considers that the second stage may last six to ten years in southern reservoirs (to latitude 50°N.), and twenty-five to thirty years in higher latitudes (above 50°N.).

General Discussion

LUND: Mr. Gilson has suggested that the lakes formed by barrages across Morecambe Bay or the Solway might eventually be biologically similar to Loch Leven, Kinross, so I would like to ask Mr. Morgan to outline the botanical situation in Loch Leven in relation to possible aquatic weed development in the barrage lakes.

MORGAN: Most of Loch Leven is less than 20 ft deep and many of the shallow parts have a sandy bottom, so that physically the conditions are similar to those in the proposed barrage lakes. There is little published information on the weeds in the loch, but dense growths of *Elodea canadensis* were reported in 1897 by the Loch Leven Angling Association and West (Flora of Scottish Lakes, VI. *Proc. R. Soc. Edin.* (1910) **30**, 65–182) lists a wide variety of plants including eight species of *Potamogeton*. Preliminary investigations in 1965 suggest that most of the submerged macrophytes have disappeared and that the few species that are left are in poor condition. This is probably associated with the prolonged blooms of blue-green algae which have occurred in the loch since about 1963 and which have greatly reduced the light penetration over a period of several months at a time. These algal blooms are in turn probably associated with the high levels of nitrate and phosphate in the inflowing streams which are mainly derived from inorganic fertilizers applied to the surrounding farmland (Fisheries of Scotland Report for 1964, pp. 125–126). Patches of emergent vegetation, *Phragmites communis*, *Polygonum amphibium* and *Eleocharis palustris*, continue to thrive around the margin of the loch. From the limited amount of information available for Loch Leven, it would seem that the question of whether macrophytes or phytoplankton predominate in the barrages will depend on the quantities of inorganic salts being contributed by the inflowing rivers which in turn will depend on the surrounding land-use. At present it is unlikely that these carry a very high concentration of minerals but with development of the area following the barrage construction this may change.

PENTELOW: Commenting in general on the work on man-made lakes. Why do we lose our ecological heads as soon as we are faced with such problems? If we alter the environment it is bound to lead to instability. The period of instability is not known, but will certainly be related to the generation time of the plants and animals concerned. When a dam is built we try to rush around remedying its immediate effects (weed growths, fisheries etc.). This (a) wastes money, and (b) involves experiments to which answers cannot be known because nature is doing things in her own way. I therefore suggest that we should not rush at immediate problems but find out first what the problem is that we really have to solve.

RZOSKA: This is all very well, but in a planned economy you want quick results. If you let reservoirs mature it takes many years. So you have to interfere. There is then a chain reaction and you have to interfere more.

GIFKINS: Which scheme is likely to be first, Morecambe Bay or Solway Firth?

GILSON: I have no idea. Two separate firms are preparing feasibility surveys. Then I suppose there has to be Treasury approval.

HUXLEY: As Regional Officer for the Nature Conservancy in South Scotland I have a particular interest in one of these barrage schemes. Specifications for feasibility studies have been submitted by the appropriate Government Departments to two firms of consulting engineers; these have been amended and tenders have now been received amounting to £300 000 for the Solway scheme and £350 000 for Morecambe Bay. It is understood that the tenders have been accepted and the engineers are now waiting for the Government decision to go ahead. It will be very unfortunate if they go ahead with one feasibility study only for we need comparable data from several estuarine areas—during the Loch Lomond scheme inquiry the engineers were asked whether they had addressed their minds to alternative proposals. What is the role of the biologist in advising governments on what decisions to take? Two views have been expressed here: (a) that nature should take its course, or (b) that if we interfere then we have to interfere more. If we take the former view we biologists will lose our position of being sought after to give reasonable advice. Biologists in advisory positions have an obligation to themselves of making certain of being involved in the investigation and planning stages, however great the difficulty of giving precise answers. My experience regarding the Loch Lomond scheme has brought out the mutual value of achieving a close working relationship with the consulting engineers.

HAIGH: I seem to have detected a note of criticism in some of the earlier contributions to the discussion, for it has been implied that civil engineers do not seek the advice of biologists sufficiently readily, and that promoters of schemes involving hydrobiological considerations do not appoint biologists as consultants at an adequately early stage in the projects. Possibly there are grounds for this criticism, but civil engineering is changing so rapidly in recent years that, as regards design work, it is becoming far less a mere technology and much more an applied science. It is now quite common practice on major works for advice to be sought from several scientists on different topics at an early stage, and to such an extent that the civil engineer sometimes feels that he has lost much of his privileged position in design and become a mere co-ordinator of the contributions by scientific specialists.

These contacts tend to emphasize the differences in training, outlook and practice between scientists and engineers. Whilst scientists can retain to a considerable extent freedom of choice in the research subjects that they study, and could abandon them if their work proved to be unproductive, the individual problems facing civil engineers arise from the projects themselves and are not of the engineers' choosing; moreover solutions, however unsatisfactory or unconvincing, have to be found, and found without unduly delaying the work or adding to its cost. As a result, to scientists, problems are welcomed as a challenge and as subjects worthy of their attention; to engineers, problems are unwelcome, except as matters of personal technical interest, because they represent things that have not been settled and which, if neglected, might easily lead to even greater difficulties.

At the end of the first session an important discussion developed on the question of how much time is required by a biologist to make a study of a proposed man-made lake in the tropics (p. 48). This was not resolved because, understandably, the scientists had in mind all the factors to be taken into account on an individual site. Nevertheless it is important to recognize that scientific advice on one aspect of a project that is submitted too late to influence practical decisions is of no value whatever and is a waste of effort; indeed the advice offered may then fall under the suspicion that it had been influenced by the decision already taken. Scientific advice therefore must be integrated within the overall programme for the project; conversely, civil engineers who are usually responsible for preparing these programmes must allow sufficient time for the scientific investigations; they can only do so with the guidance of scientists.

The distinctions between scientists and engineers is also emphasized sometimes in the form and extent of the advice offered, owing to the responsible sincerity and accuracy of scientists. Thus, in a recent example, a scientist came to a conclusion that the probability of a particular event occurring was 60% and of exactly the opposite occurring was 40%. To both scientists and engineers that is an acceptable and understandable conclusion to reach, but to their client it was of no help whatsoever. In certain instances therefore, it is necessary for a scientist to step beyond his self-imposed limits and openly to enter the field of conjecture.

Problems Associated with the Use of Man-made Lakes in the Temperate Zone

Engineering and Economic Problems of Large-scale Water Supply

FRANK LAW

Fylde Water Board, Blackpool, England

INTRODUCTION

During the past decade there have been great changes in the water supply industry. One of the most far-reaching has been the reduction of the number of undertakings at the behest of the Government in 1956. In 1956 there were 1 200 of them in England and Wales, but this number has been reduced to less than 400. In most cases the amalgamations have been advantageous and it is quite possible that there will be further drastic rationalizations in the near future.

The latest major change has been the creation of river authorities which on 1 April 1965 replaced the former River Boards with the changed emphasis on duties, in that in the Water Resources Act of 1963 they are charged:

"To take such action as . . . necessary . . . for . . . conserving, re-distributing or otherwise augmenting water resources in their area, or of transferring any such resources to the area of another river au-thority."

This change to river authorities has grown out of the deliberations of the Central Advisory Water Committee whose sub-committee on the growing demand for water produced three reports (1958, 1960, 1962).

The idea of a river regulating authority was mooted by C. A. Ris-bridger (1958) in his presidential address to the Institution of Water Engineers, and probably has blossomed at a quicker rate than its author ever dared to hope. It was helped along by the severe drought of 1959 which was closely followed by the extensive floods of 1960.

During the past six years the Surface Water Survey (formerly a department of the Ministry of Housing and Local Government and now a branch of the new Water Resources Board) has published a series of hydrological surveys of particular river basins, the order of publication presumably indicating the importance of these basins as regards water conservation and the need for development of supplies (Boulton and others, 1959–64).

161

A major concept behind many of these changes and plans is the minimum acceptable flow of a river (commonly abbreviated to M.A.F.) which
is officially described as:
> "the minimum which in the opinion of the river authority is needed for
> safeguarding the public health and for meeting (in respect both of
> quantity and quality of water) the requirements of existing lawful uses
> of the inland water, whether for agriculture, industry, water supply or
> other purposes . . ."

The determination of M.A.F.'s for key points on its rivers is one of the
main duties imposed upon the river authorities by the Water Resources
Act, 1963, and is likely to prove a very thorny problem. Certain factors
will be referred to later in this paper.

The Growth of Consumption

One of the greatest problems with which water undertakings (both
large and small) have to contend at present is the growth in consumption.
In the first report of the sub-committee of the Central Advisory Water
Committee (1958) the conclusion was reached that the rate of growth of
water consumption over the period 1955–56 was likely to be about 2·3%
per annum. Since that time the pattern of life has changed by the advent
of automatic washing machines, dish washers, etc., and most undertakings
have experienced, over the past five years, consumption growths of 4–5%
per annum and others even 8% and more.

A point of particular interest is that in many districts consumption of
water sold by meter is rising quicker than is the "domestic" component of
the supply. Prior to the Water Act of 1945 it was customary for industry
to develop its own water resources, but that Act placed the duty upon
statutory water undertakers.

A growth rate of 5% per annum may not sound spectacular but, if it
continues, it means that in the north-west, for instance, the undertakings
linked more or less to Manchester will need an extra 300 million gal per
day (m.g.d.) in the next twenty years—an amount equal to their present
consumption.

The Cost of Water

Many people contend that water is too cheap a commodity and that
if it cost more, and was sold by meter, the amount consumed would
be reduced. It is indisputable that it is cheap—the price of 2/6d. per
thousand gal (a quite usual price for the present unit for sale) is equivalent to 6¾d. per ton, stored, treated and delivered!

In the case of the Fylde Water Board (which supplies some 32 m.g.d. to a population of half-a-million in North Lancashire) the supplies have previously been from upland catchments but are now being supplemented by softened borehole water, and the unit cost of 2/3d. per thousand gallons in 1964/65 was made up as set out in the first three columns of figures in Table I. For comparison, the figures for the cheapest scheme for additional water are set out in the other three columns.

TABLE I

	Fylde Water Board 1964/65 costs*			Estimated Hellifield scheme costs. Complete scheme fully used, 85 m.g.d. for abstraction + 65 m.g.d. M.A.F.*		
	Operating costs	Debt charges	Total	Operating costs	Debt charges	Total
Supply	1·06	2·74	3·80	0·33	3·30	3·63
Treatment	2·48	1·82	4·30	3·16	2·12	5·28
Transmission	0·46	4·78	5·24	2·57	2·17	4·74
Sub-totals	4·00	9·34	13·34	6·06	7·59	13·65
Distribution	4·06	3·07	7·12			
Rents and rates	2·19	—	2·19			
Management etc.	3·86	0·07	3·93	10·52	3·14	13·66
Revenue contrib. to capital	0·42	—	0·42			
Totals	14·52	12·48	27·00	16·58	10·73	27·31

*All costs in pence per 1 000 gal.

Cost figures for other undertakings can be found in the I.M.T.A. publication entitled "Water Statistics" (1963/64). There are very wide variations in costs between individual undertakings and in general it may be said that upland sources of supply are low in operating costs but high in debt charges whilst underground sources have relatively high operating costs but low debt charges. For example, borehole schemes can be developed for capital outlays ranging from (say) £25 000 to £55 000 per 1 m.g.d. yield (Cooper, 1965). On the other hand, with upland schemes, costs of £300 000 to £400 000 per 1 m.g.d. yield are quite customary. With pumped storage schemes one may have the worst of both worlds—high capital costs (Cooper quotes £360 000 per 1 m.g.d. yield) and high running costs.

A difficulty with upland supplies is that the debt charges, already high as a lump sum, are particularly high per *unit of demand* in the initial stages of a scheme, when the demand may be only (say) 20% of the ultimate. For example in Table I the total costs of Hellifield water are very similar to the existing F.W.B. costs, but if the demand were only 20% of the ultimate the debt charges for supply would have to be multiplied by 5, because the reservoir can be constructed only as a one-stage process. Interest charges incurred during construction are often "capitalized" but once "production" commences all interest and the appropriate loan-redemption charges have to be paid in full. This often results in reservoir and pipeline schemes being "cheese-pared" to the ultimate detriment of proper development.

PROVISION OF STORAGE

An important point to remember is that a water undertaking which is facing up to its duties must be able to maintain supplies throughout a drought which may occur only once (say) in a person's lifetime. To do this it is essential to have adequate storage capacity, the nature of which will depend upon circumstances. In the case of underground supplies the storage is in the fissures and pores of the rock, or in the pores of gravel deposits. These stocks of water are not as easy to measure and to visualize as those which exist on the surface. The usual method is by the interpretation of the results of pumping tests and long pumping runs, in conjunction with the records of strata encountered during the drilling of boreholes. Water bearing aquifers are of two types: those in which the water table is unconfined, and those in which the water is confined by overlying impervious (or nearly impervious) strata. Unconfined aquifers definitely provide more storage for water than do confined aquifers.

Storage for surface supplies can be divided into three categories (Bleasdale and others, 1962):

(a) *Direct-supply impounding reservoirs*, often found in the higher valleys, from which the water is piped (usually by gravity) to the points of consumption.

(b) *River regulating reservoirs*, used to maintain the flow in the river below the reservoir, so that water can be abstracted many miles downstream, preferably near the sea or just above some other point of gross pollution.

(c) *Intake- or pumped-storage reservoirs*, which are built on a site which is geologically suitable but without an adequate catchment.

In all cases the amount of storage required to maintain a specified yield is dependent upon the characteristics of the river from which the reservoir is fed or which it regulates, but in general there is a law of rapidly diminishing returns for greater storage provided, and, of the three types, river regulating reservoirs can give the greatest yields for a given amount of storage.

This generalization regarding river-regulating reservoirs depends very greatly, however, upon the figures to be adopted for M.A.F.

This topic of M.A.F. has been ventilated quite fully over the past few years, notably in papers by Boulton (1965) and Lovett, Houghton, Southgate, Nixon, Hoather and Lyon (all 1964), but practically all of the above papers deal with the cases of polluted rivers, where the water is re-used time after time. There are, however, other rivers, particularly in the northern counties of England, where rainfall is high, pollution is negligible and the main criteria for M.A.F. are amenity and game fishing. Baxter (1961, 1962) has suggested proportions of the A.D.F. (average daily flow) depending upon the time of the year, but there is very grave danger that one-eighth A.D.F. and one-quarter A.D.F. etc., abstracted from Baxter's suggestions, may be used rather rigidly. The following figures for the Hellifield Scheme on the River Ribble illustrate these points.

Proposed reservoir   18 000 million gal capacity
As direct supply reservoir Gross yield   95 m.g.d.
                            Assume as compensation water   20
                            Net yield for supply   75
As river regulating reservoir
   with abstraction 20 miles downstream at point where average daily flow (A.D.F.) is 400 m.g.d.
   Flow, before abstraction, can be sustained at 150 m.g.d. by discharges from the reservoir.
If M.A.F. = 50 m.g.d. ($\frac{1}{8}$ of A.D.F.) Permissible abstraction
                            for supply   = 100 m.g.d.
If M.A.F. = 75 m.g.d.   ,,   = 75 m.g.d.
                                                   (same as for
                                                   direct supply)
If M.A.F. = 100 m.g.d. ($\frac{1}{4}$ of A.D.F.)   ,,   = only 50 m.g.d.

A far better method for ascertaining the water required by fish has been pioneered by Stewart (1964) at the Lancashire River Authority, whose instrumentation on the River Leven (flowing out of Lake Windermere) promises to give very interesting and illuminating results and should be replicated on other salmon and sea trout rivers. The difficulty is going to be one of analysing adequately the shoals of data so as to arrive at valid conclusions.

Whatever the outcome of these investigations, whether they show more water or less is needed for game fish, it behoves water abstractors and river authorities to endeavour to make such water available at the appropriate times.

Unfortunately, there seems to be a tendency to make the M.A.F. too rigid—indeed to have only one fixed value to cover the whole year—but it is to be hoped that common sense rather than legalism will prevail.

THE COST OF PROVIDING STORAGE

Site conditions (both topographical and geographical) determine the cost of providing storage, and therefore there is great variation in costs per million gallons stored. For dams built in the last twenty years the prices have ranged from about £150 per million gallons impounded to twenty times that figure, but the average for a representative number of post-war dams works out at about £370 per million gallons stored. It will be interesting to see how the greatly publicized proposed estuarial barrages will measure up to this "yardstick". Figures of £30 million to £50 million, and a usable volume of £30 000 million gal in the top 5 ft have been mentioned for the Morecambe Bay barrage. These figures work out at £1 000 to £1 670 per million gallons usable storage—three to five times the post-war average. The 18 000 million gal reservoir instanced for Hellifield is estimated to cost about £6 million (i.e. £330 per million gal which is just below the average). If the natural flow in a dryish spell (not the extreme D.W.F.) drops to about 35 m.g.d., and the *sustainable* flow with the river regulation is 150 m.g.d., then 115 m.g.d. improvement in the river averages £520 000 for every 10 m.g.d. improvement. This sum is, therefore, the capital cost of every 10 m.g.d. added to the M.A.F.; constituting an annual cost of approximately £35 000. This would seem to justify a considerable amount of research before M.A.F.'s are determined.

QUALITY OF WATER WITH RIVER REGULATION

It is often claimed for river-regulating reservoirs that, by their construction and use, the flow in the rivers below them will be benefited. Doubtless this will be the case in *polluted* rivers, but in the case of very clean rivers the presence of a large reservoir may be a great disadvantage.

In a *"natural river"* the water may be highly coloured and turbid in flood times, but this colour and turbidity often clears rapidly when the flow subsides. If, however, on such a river a reservoir is interposed all the water therein will become turbid and coloured, and this may be very detrimental to the amenity value of the river downstream.

It may, therefore, be found on clear and sparkling rivers that *off-river storage* is preferable to river regulation.

It is sometimes contended, e.g. Baxter (1962), that water discharged to a river from the reservoir should be taken from the top rather than from the bottom. Temperature and oxygen-content deficiencies of bottom water can be corrected within some 200 yd of the outlet of a reservoir, and on balance the constant discharge of bottom water seems better in the long run, avoiding as it certainly does the building up of a large stock of poor-quality water at the bottom of the reservoir to be disturbed at the time of autumnal turnover, to the detriment of the rest of the water.

The Cost of Treatment of Water

Treatment costs depend very greatly upon the nature of the raw water and the quality demanded or expected by the consumers. In this respect industrial consumers are often more difficult to satisfy than are the domestic ones. Labour and chemical costs usually amount to about 1·5d. per thousand gal for fairly clean upland waters rising to about 3·5d. where the water has to undergo more sophisticated processes.

Capital costs for treatment plants of 10 m.g.d. capacity and over seem to average about £40 000 per 1 m.g.d. capacity which may result in debt charges of 2·1d. per 1 000 gal. There seems to be great scope for the comparison of capital costs of these plants and the evolution of more efficient coagulation tanks and simpler filtration installations, particularly for the clean waters found in the natural lakes in the Lake District (and possibly ultimately to be found in some of the man-made lakes).

The Cost of Transporting and Lifting Water

As schemes of water supply become larger, the distance for the water to be carried usually becomes greater; and with the more general movement of abstraction points down-river, or even to the tidal limit, the height of lift to be produced by pumping becomes greater.

Study of the economics is facilitated by dividing the pumping into two components: (a) the actual static lift, and (b) the friction required to propel the water along a horizontal pipeline.

Electricity is the most frequent form of power employed nowadays, and the economics of pumping are complicated by the various electricity tariffs. If pumping can be avoided in certain daytime periods in weekdays from mid-November to mid-February the cost per unit of electricity may be reduced by one-third (1·25d. per unit reduced to 0·8d. per unit for about 80% load factor).

The cost of lifting water is roughly 0·6d. per thousand gal per 100 ft lifted (winter and summer) and 0·4d. per thousand gal per 100 ft lifted if winter peaks are avoided.

Regarding transmission through a pipeline, for a given type of pipe and a constant hydraulic gradient the carrying capacity is roughly proportional to $D^{2·5}$ (where D is the diameter) but the cost of the pipe and laying is proportional only to $D^{1 \cdot 2}$ (Lapworth, 1943). Consequently, it is cheaper (per unit volume) to transport large quantities of water than it is to move small quantities. The difficulty is one of finance in the early stages of development of a scheme.

The debt charges per unit volume for a given pipeline are proportional to Q^{-1}, whilst the power charges are proportional to Q^2. The sum of these drop to a minimum value at the "optimum" flow rate and then rise again.

The "minimum" cost of pumping water through "level" pipelines 36 in. in diameter amounts to 2·07d. per 1 000 gal for every 10 miles length and occurs at an "optimum" flow of 20 m.g.d. This can be compared with 1·12d. per 1 000 gal for every 10 miles length for a pipeline 72 in. in diameter for which optimum conditions are at 85 m.g.d. Provided the initial stages can be managed financially, it is more economic to use one 72 in. diameter pipeline than multiple pipelines each 36 in. diameter, once a flow of 30 m.g.d. has been exceeded. If economic conditions in the first few years dictated an initial 36 in. pipeline it would be more economic to follow this by one 72 in. diameter rather than have two, three or more subsequent ones each 36 in. diameter (Risbridger, 1955).

These figures may not seem large but the distances involved can be quite great. For example, water for the north-west from a Solway barrage would have to come some 90 miles round the coast to Lancaster. Through a 72 in. diameter pipeline this transportation would cost about 10d. per thousand gal (assuming no ups and downs in the pipeline).

SAVINGS EFFECTED BY INTEGRATION OF DIVERSE RESOURCES

The amalgamation of undertakings into larger units can offer the opportunities to save quite considerable sums of money by the integration of diverse resources.

Upland reservoirs have usually been developed on the basis of their reliable yields as separate entities, this reliable yield being the supply which can be given continuously throughout a drought which may recur (on the average) only once every century (say). In all the other 99 years there will be surplus water in the reservoir.

In the case of the Fylde Water Board, their major reservoir has a reliable yield of 12 m.g.d., but plans are in hand to take up to 28 m.g.d. from it in wet periods, the deficiency in drier periods being made up from boreholes in the Bunter sandstone (Law, 1965). There may not be many undertakings with underground and upland sources in such close proximity, but in the future it may be worthwhile to arrange amalgamations with this specific purpose in mind.

This suggested overdrawing of upland reservoirs has not been sufficiently appreciated in the past.

Many small undertakings in the north-west with upland reservoirs near at hand have, of course, been in the custom of overdrawing their reservoirs (sometimes quite unconsciously) and it would appear that the ultimate large-scale implementation of their future demands, whether it be from Morecambe Bay barrage or a Solway barrage, or from Hellifield, Winster or Killington, the implementation could be made more economic by encouraging them to draw water from this new source only when their existing supplies could no longer be overdrawn. Pumping and treatment running costs on these large new schemes are estimated to cost at least 6d. per thousand gal, and probably at least 4d. or 5d. of this could be saved by keeping this plant idle in wet periods and overdrawing existing resources. No doubt many people would frown upon the idea of spending large sums of money on a major scheme and then only using it for 10, 20 or 30% of the time thereafter, but such idleness could save the country much money.

AUGMENTATION OF SUPPLY BY SEA-WATER DISTILLATION

Nowadays no paper regarding water supplies can be complete without mentioning desalination of sea water. The topic has become rather hackneyed, but an aspect which should be borne in mind, is that desalination can be an economic auxiliary to surface resources in certain conditions, such as in Guernsey in the Channel Islands; indeed it is the extreme case for the economics of integrated supplies.

The Guernsey distillation plant was installed four years ago with a capacity of 0·5 m.g.d. to augment the existing surface resources which yielded up to 4 m.g.d. (Morgan, 1961). The debt charges on the additional 0·5 m.g.d. work out at 3/0d. per thousand gallons and running costs at 7/6d. per thousand gallons. It is noteworthy, however, that, in the four years since construction, the plant has been run for only 3 months (i.e. a load factor of only 7%). During the remainder of the time the 0·5 m.g.d. extra water has been available from the surface resources by overdrawing of the reservoirs, and the cost of the treatment of this water has probably been only about 2d. per thousand gal. The average running costs of the additional 0·5 m.g.d. water made available by the construction of the distillation plant has, therefore, been 7% of 7/6d., plus 2d. (say approximately 8d.). Consequently, the total cost of the extra 0·5 m.g.d. water in Guernsey has been about 3/8d. per thousand gal. Morgan (1961) has estimated that reservoir storage on Guernsey costs £5 000 per million gal stored, and at such high rates the debt charges on a reservoir capable of augmenting the yield by 0·5 m.g.d. would have amounted to about 8/0d.

170   FRANK LAW

per thousand gal. On the nearby island of Jersey a reservoir has recently been constructed at a cost of £2 800 per million gal stored, and even at this lower figure the debt charges alone amount to 5/0d. per thousand gallons in Guernsey's catchment run-off conditions.

It would seem, therefore, that Guernsey was well justified in adopting sea-water distillation *in conjunction with upland resources.*

CONCLUDING REMARKS

Many major water supply schemes will have to be developed in the near future, and the cost will be large. It behoves everyone to endeavour to keep these costs as low as possible, commensurate with proper respect for amenity, recreational needs, and the health and well-being of the community.

REFERENCES

Baxter, G. (1961). River utilization and the preservation of migratory fish life. *Proc. Instn civ. Engrs* **18**, 225–244.

Baxter, G. (1962). Preservation of fish life, amenities and facilities for recreation. Institution of Civil Engineers Symposium on Conservation of Water Resources in U.K., pp. 59–65.

Bleasdale, A., Boulton, A. G., Ineson, J. and Law, F. (1962). Study and assessment of water resources. Institution of Civil Engineers Symposium on Conservation of Water Resources in U.K., pp. 121–136.

Boulton, A. G. (1965). Minimum acceptable flow. *J. Instn Wat. Engrs* **19**, 15–31.

Boulton, A. G. *et al.* (1959–64). "Hydrological Survey". Ministry of Housing and Local Government, H.M.S.O., London. (1959) Great Ouse Basin; (1960) River Severn Basin; (1961) Essex Rivers and Stow; (1961) Rivers Wear and Tees; (1962) River Lee Basin; (1963) East Anglian Rivers; (1964) Kent Rivers; (1964) North Lancashire Rivers.

Central Advisory Water Committee (1958–62). Report of Sub-Committee on the Growing Demand for Water. H.M.S.O., London. (1958) Interim Report; (1960) Second Report; (1962) Final Report.

Cooper, C. (1965). Present trends in public water supply. *J. Instn munic. Engrs* pp. 104–106.

Hoather, R. C. (1964). The successive re-use of river water: its effects and its limitations. *J. Instn Wat. Engrs* **18**.

Houghton, G. U. (1964). The quality of river water as a factor in the determination of minimum acceptable flows. *J. Instn Wat. Engrs* **18**.

Institute of Municipal Treasurers and Accountants (1964). "Water Statistics 1963/64".

Lapworth, F. C. (1943). Discussion on: Mainlaying, estimates and costs analysis, by E. W. Denholm. *Trans Instn Wat. Engrs* **49**, 65.

Law, F. (1965). Integrated use of diverse resources. *J. Instn Wat. Engrs* **19**, 413–436.

Lovett, M. (1964). The quality of river water as a factor in the determination of minimum acceptable flows. *J. Instn Wat. Engrs* **18**, 198–205.

Lyon, A. L. (1964). The quality of river water as a factor in the determination of minimum acceptable flows. *J. Instn Wat. Engrs* 18, 215–224.

Morgan, W. H. (1961). Augmentation of supply by sea-water distillation. *J. Instn Wat. Engrs* 15, 265–281.

Nixon, M. (1964). The successive re-use of river water; its effect and its limitations. *J. Instn Wat. Engrs* 18, 225–231.

Risbridger, C. A. (1955). Discussion in *J. Instn Wat. Engrs* 9, 410–413.

Risbridger, C. A. (1958). Presidential address. *J. Instn Wat. Engrs* 12, 237–246.

Southgate, B. A. (1964). The quality of river water as a factor in the determination of minimum acceptable flows. *J. Instn Wat. Engrs* 18, 219–224.

Stewart, L. (1964). The impact of the Water Resources Act 1963 on fisheries. Proceedings of London Conference of Salmon and Trout Association, 1964, pp. 1–19. (See also: Recording river fish movements. *Engineer, Lond.* 18 June 1965.)

Discussion

LUND: Are there any other sites which will produce as much water as the Morecambe Bay barrage scheme?

LAW: It has been stated that Morecambe Bay Barrage would provide 30 000 million gal storage for water supply purposes. There seems to be an alternative site available in the Killington area between the Lake District and the River Lune. This might hold 40 000 million gal (or even more) and at such a site the work could be carried out in stages and at a final cost of less than one-quarter of the cost of an estuarial barrage.

HUXLEY: With the development of off-peak electricity is it possible to cut costs by using off-peak electricity for pumps?

LAW: Killington is about 700 ft above sea-level and the water would have to be pumped there from the Lune or from the Lake District rivers, but it would then flow *by gravity* to the populated parts of Lancashire. This arrangement would permit advantage to be taken of "off-peak" electricity tariffs—in the months of November to February abstraction would not take place at peak demand times on weekdays and this would cut electricity costs by at least 30%. This advantage could not be gained with estuarial barrages because the storage would be at sea-level, and pumping would have to be continuous.

DREW: Mr. Law's paper does not reflect thinking on anything like a national scale about the future scale of water demands. He prefers to nibble at rather than take one good bite at the problem. I would agree with him that some assessment criterion must be evolved, e.g. storage volume per unit of capital investment, and would ask him not to overlook the fact that the Solway Barrage (of say $1\frac{1}{4}$ miles) compares favourably on this criterion with any other proposition he cares to cite. Moreover, in one proposition, it could meet the national needs to the end of the century and beyond.

Further, as soon as we think in terms of bulk transfer of substantial quantities of water—as would be the case if we can raise our sights to the concept of a national water grid—then even transport charges from Solway for

Manchester and the north-west become comparable with the 4d. per thousand gal he cites for other small local-scale schemes.

It really was not very scientific, or consistent of Mr. Law to assert in one breath that there was an abundance of upland sources for years to come, and then to say that minimum acceptable flow data have yet to be determined. Also, do we really want to live in a society in which each trickle from the mountains and hills is meticulously limited to the "minimum acceptable flow"? I for one want to see maximum variety preserved in our countryside with rivers large and small flowing largely uninterrupted to the sea before man intervenes to secure water for his domestic and industrial activities.

LAW: I strongly disagree. It is impossible to transport water from Solway to Manchester for 4d. per thousand gal, whatever the scale, and "nibbling" at resources is better than bankruptcy.

BISWAS: Mr. Law states that water consumption is rising faster in some districts where sold by meter than the "domestic component of the supply", which presumably is unmetered. Has any study been conducted on this problem? For example, would not the consumption of water have risen still higher in those metered areas without metering? In some communities a 40% reduction in water use has been achieved by the introduction of metering (Linsley and Franzini (1964). "Water Resources Engineering", p. 409, McGraw Hill, New York).

Nuclear craters have opened up a whole new vista for water storage, for surface water or for ground-water recharge. An advantage is flexibility of location, a disadvantage that water has to be pumped out from the reservoir as gravity release cannot work. Tests on craters are being carried out at present (1965) in Nevada.

Contrary to Mr. Law, I do not believe that the desalination of sea water "has become rather hackneyed". If an efficient and economic process for conversion can be evolved, the problem of water shortage can be eliminated. The cost of conversion has steadily come down, from $5.00 per 1 000 U.S. Gallons in 1950 to $2.00 in 1955, $1.00 in 1960 and an anticipated 22–30 cents in 1966. Desalinization is bound to play a significant part in the future because the cost of conversion is coming down compared with the ever-increasing costs of obtaining water by "conventional" means.

LAW: We have conducted extensive studies of consumption after the metering of consumers, particularly farms. Prior to metering in 1951, farms paid on an acreage basis. Eleven farms (av. 85 acres each) paid an average of £15 per year. Upon metering the cost jumped to £23 and is now £69 although the unit cost of water has gone up by only 35%. Their consumption has gone up 4·6 times (i.e. by 8·3% per year), despite metering. To meter *domestic* supplies would increase the cost of water by 50%. The cost of fixing a meter on a domestic supply is about £16, and to do this for all the 177 000 customers in the Fylde area would cost something like £3 million.

Maintaining the Safety and Quality
of Water Supplies

G. U. HOUGHTON

South Essex Waterworks Co., Colchester, England

INTRODUCTION

The basic obligations of a water undertaking may be simply defined. It may be said that the public supply must be adequate both as to volume and pressure, be hygienically safe, not displeasing aesthetically and not too hard or mineralized for domestic purposes. In this country hygienic safety is largely a bacteriological question but, in addition, the water should not contain metallic ions or other substances which might confer either short-term or long-term toxicity. With the tendency for the impurity of many surface sources to increase, considerations of water quality and treatment are becoming of growing importance and they increasingly impinge on the engineering, hydrological and economic problems of supplying enough water to meet the rising standards of living.

The water undertaker is in the position of having to choose his treatment processes according to the quality of his source and these processes are themselves tending to become of increasing complexity and cost. He must therefore have the best possible understanding of the quality of his raw water, especially as to the most onerous conditions liable to occur: these latter will decide the scope of the treatment required to meet all eventualities and have an important bearing on the economics of the matter. In the present context we must therefore ask how the impoundment of a raw water in a reservoir ("man-made lake"), and any secondary uses of the water for recreation, will modify the situation in so far as matters of quality are concerned.

In trying to answer this question for a new reservoir, an inherent difficulty at once arises in that one has got to try and predict what the quality of the impounded water is likely to be. Decisions as to treatment may have to be taken at an early stage of planning, probably before the reservoir is filled. And, indeed, it cannot be assumed, at least in productive reservoirs, that the character of the water in the early stages will be representative of conditions many years ahead.

173

Broad and helpful generalizations may, of course, be made. If the water is from a barren rocky catchment then biological production is likely to be low; conversely, productive waters and sites will almost certainly need extensive filtration plant to cope with algal and other growth. Judging just how far biological production will go is obviously extremely difficult. The best that can be done may well be to learn lessons from previous similar schemes and here lies the value of continuous analytical records for new impoundments. British data of this sort are fragmentary but there is a certain amount of information available (Thompson, 1946; Oliver, 1948; Houghton, 1954; Hammerton, 1959a; Dowling, 1964).

In 1964 the U.S. Public Health Service published a review of the great volume of literature available and this may be commended to anyone interested in studying the overall picture. It reveals the need for more research and for a general synthesis of what is already known so that confident practical decisions can be made in any particular case. As the authors pertinently remark: "With so much literature on the subject, one might wonder whether problems could still exist; but many do".

Previous speakers in this symposium will doubtless deal with the highly complex physico-chemical and biological relationships on which depend the ultimate character of the water in store. The discussion which follows can only deal with a few of those facets of water quality which are important in stored waters from the point of view of the water authority.

BACTERIAL IMPURITY

In the temperate zones by far the greatest hygienic risk to public water supplies is contamination by enteric and dysentery organisms, such as may derive from human excremental pollution. These organisms may be present either in the dejecta of those having the disease or from "carriers" who have no clinical symptoms and whose identity is probably quite unknown. Surface supplies, and in fact all water supplies except those of minimal size, must therefore have facilities for sterilization, usually chlorination though ozonization may sometimes be employed. Regular bacteriological examination of the water is also necessary, the universal criterion of safety being the presence or absence of coliform organisms, and particularly of *Escherichia coli I*, the typical organism present in the intestine of warm-blooded animals.

To a variable degree all raw surface waters are liable to contain coliform bacteria and though it does not follow that these always derive from human or other excrement, if they are *E. coli I* there can be no doubt that such is the case. The ecology of coliform bacteria is still obscure in some respects and the water undertaker therefore aims to keep his supply free from coliform organisms of every type. Since rivers are the natural channel for the disposal of sewage works effluents it is hardly surprising that faecal coliform bacteria are abundant in the lower reaches of most British rivers, but the organisms may also derive from general surface run-off. As an example, the Thames at Walton in 1962 (Metropolitan Water Board, 40th Report) had an average monthly $E.$ $coli$ count varying from 412 to 11 400 per 100 ml and some figures for the River Stour (Essex) are given in Table I.

Fortunately intestinal bacteria tend to die out comparatively quickly in a lake or reservoir, and how great this natural purification can be on long storage is well illustrated by the results obtained in the South Essex Waterworks Company's Abberton reservoir, for which some typical figures are also given in Table I. For shorter periods of storage the reduction in bacterial content may not be so great but even a few days retention can have a valuable effect and storage alone has long been recognized as an important barrier against bacterial pollution.

It is against this background that one must view any pollutional hazard arising from recreational usage of a reservoir, especially a large one. Pollution of this sort would have to be heavy in the extreme to be comparable with that normal to the influents of many lowland reservoirs. However, it will be realized that with lowland reservoirs very full purification facilities are invariably provided and are an integral part of the scheme. If such treatment plant is available and in continuous use it is almost impossible to conceive that recreational pollution of a bacterial nature could lead to a deterioration in the quality of the final supply. A recent authoritative report by the Institution of Water Engineers on the Recreational Use of Waterworks (1963) has stated "where water is filtered and sterilized it should be possible to allow the public to enjoy whatever recreational facilities can be provided".

On the other hand, bacterial purity is so vital that it would be wrong to imply that pollution of any sort is to be lightly regarded; quite rightly, many water authorities in the past have viewed with disfavour anything which might remotely affect the purity of their supplies. Such an attitude has especial justification where the stored water is of good quality, as from an upland source, so that extensive purification plant is not otherwise necessary. It is also true that it is better for a water undertaking to be over-cautious about purity than the reverse. Each case must be considered on its merits but what is widely recognized is that any secondary use of the lake must be in the nature of a privilege and only granted provided strict supervision can be effected at all times. The implementation of such a policy involves considerable effort and some

TABLE I

Some Typical Analytical Results for Abberton Reservoir (Essex)

Capacity to T.W.L. 5 659 million gal.

(Chemical results as p.p.m.)	Main influent (R. Stour)* October–May 1961–62 and 1962–63			Outflowing water 1962 (Average retention 9 months)		
	Minimum	Maximum	Average	Minimum	Maximum	Average
Turbidity (I.W.E.)	1·4	26·6	7·0	0·8	9·0	3·1
Colour (Hazen)	7	21·0	14·5	7	13	9·8
Free ammonia (NH_3)	0·01	1·21	0·20	0·01	0·15	0·053
Total oxidized nitrogen	2·9	8·9	5·33	0·2	5·0	2·38
Phosphate (PO_4)	0·22	0·70	0·45	Undetectable	0·09	0·018
Hardness, total	334	444	389	236	312	271
carbonate	185	286	248	106	164	137
Colony ct. (1 day/37°C) per ml	125	3 000	827	5	500	84
Colony ct. (3 days/20°C) per ml	6 500	430 000	65 800	35	10 000	1 485
Presumptive coliform count (M.P.N.) per 100 ml	230	230 000	25 200	0	620	82
E. coli I. (M.P.N.) per 100 ml	62	62 000	5 470	0	620	28

* River Stour normally constitutes 80–90% of the reservoir influent.

cost: a most useful guide to the practical problems which arise is provided by the I.W.E. report (1963) to which reference has already been made.

PHYSICAL AND CHEMICAL IMPURITY

When a surface water is stored its quality may change markedly to an extent dependent on its initial impurity, the time of storage, the topography of the reservoir and the climatic conditions. Some of these changes may be favourable to the waterworks, notably the bacteriological improvement mentioned above, but some may be unwelcome. Brief comment on some of the physical and chemical factors may be helpful on the present occasion.

BENEFICIAL CHANGES

A particularly valuable function of a storage reservoir is that it serves to balance out the peak level of many constituents, notably turbidity, colour, hardness and ammonia; also, a very important feature in river schemes is that it affords dilution of any accidental spillage or excessive discharge of any industrial waste to the water course. Apart from any balancing effect, inorganic turbidity will settle out or coagulate; ammonia and nitrate will tend to disappear as a result of plant assimilation or bacterial oxidation or reduction and denitrification processes; phosphate content may fall greatly, probably by co-precipitation on ferric hydroxide and/or calcium carbonate; synthetic anionic detergent derived from sewage will suffer partial bacterial degradation. All such balancing and self-purification effects offer much operational advantage to the waterworks since the treatment plant does not have to cope with sudden fluctuations in water quality and has to deal with a lower level of impurity throughout. As only one example, loss of free ammonia is something desirable if free-residual chlorination is practised.

Where the reservoir influent has high carbonate hardness, decomposition of bicarbonate will occur if storage is sufficiently long, either through biological agency or by slow loss of carbon dioxide to the atmosphere. This effect has been noted in several British reservoirs (Hornby, 1947; Whitehead, 1948; Houghton, 1954), and constitutes a great economic asset if the water has to be softened.

These effects are, again, particularly well shown in the Essex reservoirs at Abberton and Hanningfield where hard polluted river waters have to be utilized in conjunction with long storage periods owing to the very low dry-weather flows in the East Anglian rivers. Some typical results are shown in Table I.

ADVERSE CHANGES

No doubt the most important adverse change which may affect the
physical and chemical character of a stored water is the depletion of
dissolved oxygen resulting from stagnation or thermal stratification.
The associated anaerobiosis can lead to objectionable taste and odour in
the supply, increased chlorine demand and high ammonia, iron and manganese content. It would appear that this trouble is generally of short
duration in waterworks but it can be fairly severe and much thought is
being given to the avoidance of stratification in waterworks reservoirs.
An excellent account of the problem in the London reservoirs, in connexion with thermocline control, has been given by Ridley (1964).

Mention may also be made of the trouble which may occur through
pick-up of manganese during storage, leading to deposition of black
manganese oxides in the distribution system. This problem can be rather
troublesome since not only is manganese somewhat difficult to remove
but even 0·1 p.p.m. of Mn in a public supply can cause complaint of
staining of plumbing fixtures and fabrics, besides being undesirable in
other ways. The mechanism by which manganese content increases during storage is not too well understood although bottom deposits are
doubtless implicated. Trouble arises particularly easily where the reservoir site includes strata rich in the element: thus in the Weir Wood
reservoir on the Ashdown Beds, manganese contents up to 1·7 p.p.m.
were experienced in the early years of the scheme (Dowling, 1964).

MICROBIOLOGICAL (OTHER THAN BACTERIAL) IMPURITY

The foregoing may perhaps be sufficient to indicate that storage can
offer substantial advantages to the treatment works from a chemical and
bacteriological point of view, provided that thermal stratification does
not introduce complications. Probably, however, the greatest drawback
which storage offers to the waterworks operator is the development of
planktonic growth where the water is biologically productive. Such
growth in the reservoir will tend to offset the removal of turbidity which
would otherwise occur and will necessitate heavy expenditure on filtration plant.

The designing of treatment plant which will give a reliable output
whatever the algal contingency is by no means easy. While algae may
promote taste troubles, their main effect is at the filtration stage. Some
organisms may be very difficult to remove by coagulation and, with or
without coagulation, difficulties can arise either through very rapid filter
blockage or, conversely, filter penetration; in the latter event the algae
spoil the clarity of the filtrate and may lead to other complications in the

distribution system. It would seem that the problem of algal growth in water supplies will grow in importance in this country as more water has to be taken from productive lowland rivers into storage reservoirs and will have much bearing on the type of treatment to be adopted.

The effects of algal growth in coagulation and filtration are closely related both to the identity and morphology of the organisms concerned and the exact method of purification being used. For instance, sand grading will govern the depth of penetration and the effect on head-loss in the bed. Filamentous planktonic forms will obviously be easiest to remove but will be retained at the top of the filter, eventually as a dense mat causing rapid blockage. At the other extreme small unicellular algae, often of nannoplankton size, will penetrate far deeper, especially if they are motile, and may indeed pass right through. Again, light and flocculent Cyanophyceae are both difficult to coagulate out in conventional equipment and easily break up to give penetrating particles.

It would be inappropriate here to make more than passing mention of the processes used for handling algal-bearing waters. Broadly speaking there are three alternatives available, all of which are usually supplemented by chlorination before or after treatment:

(a) Micro-screening.
(b) Double-sand filtration.
(c) Coagulation followed by rapid sand filtration.

Each of these processes has its merits but capital and operational costs differ widely and to the author's knowledge no rigid economic appraisal has ever been published, particularly as between (b) and (c). The problem is of especial import in southern England, where algal problems are most common, and here those concerned with treating stored waters, notably the Metropolitan Water Board, have mainly preferred to rely on the time-honoured double-sand filtration. The Board currently filter over 300 million gal/day by this method and have decided to follow the same procedure at their new (108 million gal/day) Lee Bridge works (Metropolitan Water Board, 1964); the South Essex Waterworks Co. have recently commissioned a 26 million gal/day plant using the same system. The merits of double-sand filtration are its simplicity, freedom from sludge disposal problems, the "built-in" barrier which the slow sand stage offers against bacterial pollution, and almost complete freedom from algal penetration; the cost of the structures is, however, very high.

The issue between double-sand filtration and coagulation methods has nevertheless not finally been resolved, since several new procedures are coming forward. It may well be that improved coagulation techniques (e.g. using polyelectrolytes) and rapid filtration methods (e.g. using

G

mixed anthracite–sand beds) will alter the picture. If they do, coagulation methods could become standard in this country for stored waters as they already are for direct intake schemes.

LIMITATION OF ALGAL PRODUCTION IN RESERVOIRS

If algal production is likely to be an important factor in a waterworks scheme incorporating storage it is desirable that, from the outset, everything possible should be done to minimize growth. Here, as with all other problems of water pollution, prevention is better than cure. It is true that algicides may be employed to eradicate growth or prevent its development but they are not an unmixed blessing and much further basic study of their use is needed. A few of the problems involved in algicidal treatment may be listed: even application of the chemical on a large impoundment of variable depth, and the avoidance of high local concentrations, may be difficult; fish life must not be affected; secondary growths, possibly tolerant to the chemical, may appear; the range of chemicals which can be tolerated on hygienic grounds in a water supply reservoir is very limited; algal species differ in respect of the toxic dose required and this may also be dependent on the chemistry of the water.

If the new site is initially covered with fertile soil, perhaps farmland, it would seem logical that this must be an important factor in increasing algal production and also biochemical deoxygenation, at any rate in the early years of the scheme. Here again there appears to be a lack of rigid knowledge as to the importance of native bottom deposits relative to the productive capability of the inflowing water. The ideal is clearly to remove the top soil and sometimes this is carried out, either incidentally to the construction of the reservoir or as a deliberate policy. On a large site soil stripping will be expensive and there is the question of disposal of the spoil. At Chew Valley lake (4 500 million gal) it was estimated (Hammerton, 1959b) that stripping all soil would cost nearly 10% of constructional costs and it was not carried out: however, subsequent studies suggested that a limited programme of stripping adjacent to the dam would have been worthwhile.

Another matter which has already attracted attention in America (U.S. Dept. Health, 1960) and in Europe (Hasler, 1947) is how far contamination by domestic drainage (sewage effluents) is of importance in the eutrophication of reservoirs. In the past, the main criterion for an effluent has been whether it would create a physical and aesthetic nuisance in the receiving watercourse, especially whether it would deoxygenate the stream. With the increasing use of lowland rivers for water supply, and the concomitant increase in the proportion of effluent which such rivers may carry, wider issues arise. One of these is the question of how far sewage accentuates algal proliferation, and since river schemes in Britain will increasingly rely on storage, perhaps in the form of regulating reservoirs, the matter merits further attention.

There can be no doubt that an effluent well purified by current standards will contain an abundant supply of the major plant nutrients (nitrogen, phosphorus and potassium), and possibly also other trace elements and micro-nutrients of significance. Zinc, for example, has been shown to be present in settled sewage in appreciable amount (Water Pollution Research Board, 1962). There is also well documented evidence in at least one case, that of the Zürich-Zee (Hasler, 1947), that urban drainage has led to increased biological production and changes in fish life: deterioration has also been noticed in Lake Constance (Lehn, 1964). It does not, however, follow that because productivity may be increased by raising the level of nutrients in a relatively clean water, such as that of a mountain lake, sewage effluent would exert a preponderant effect in a lowland reservoir, already receiving abundant nutrient from normal run-off or the reservoir site itself. The practical implications of this problem for some waterworks will readily be appreciated.

Shortage of water is leading to pressure for the greater re-use of sewage effluent; whereas previously there was a tendency in this country to divert major sewage effluents below the point of waterworks intake, there is now apt to be more emphasis on the importance of incorporating the effluents in the water cycle so as to conserve supplies. How far such re-use would increase difficulties in the management and purification of the water, or whether it would involve provision of extra filtration facilities to cope with peaks of algal growth, and whether the extra cost would warrant the extra yield, are all questions which can be very pertinent to the water technologist. It is likely that for a long time ahead every case will have to be decided according to local circumstance but more systematic information as to the effects of eutrophication in lakes used for water supply is much to be desired.

References

Dowling, L. T. (1964). Seven years experience of Weir Wood reservoir. *Proc. Soc. Wat. Treat. Exam.* **13**, 335.

Hammerton, D. (1959a). A biological and chemical study of Chew Valley Lake. *Proc. Soc. Wat. Treat. Exam.* **8**, 87.

Hammerton, D. (1959b). A biological and chemical study of Chew Valley Lake. *Proc. Soc. Wat. Treat. Exam.* **8**, 126.

Hasler, A. D. (1947). Eutrophication of lakes by domestic drainage. *Ecology* **58**, 383.

Hornby, F. P. (1947). *J. Instn Wat. Engrs* **1**, 407.

Houghton, G. U. (1954). Some biological and chemical problems in a new and shallow reservoir. *Proc. Soc. Wat. Treat. Exam.* **3**, 8.

Institution of Water Engineers (1963). Final Report on Recreational Use of Waterworks.

Lehn, H. (1964). The reduction of the depth of visibility in Lake Constance since 1920. *Wat. Pollut. Res. Abstr.* no. 1455.

Metropolitan Water Board (1961–62). 40th Report of Director of Water Examination, p. 117.

Metropolitan Water Board (1964). 61st Annual Report.

Oliver, G. C. S. (1948). Biology of Eye Brook reservoir. *J. Instn Wat. Engrs* **2**, 163.

Ridley, J. E. (1964). Thermal stratification and thermocline control in storage reservoirs. *Proc. Soc. Wat. Treat. Exam.* **13**, 275.

Thompson, R. W. S. (1946). The biology of Ladybower reservoir. *Trans. Instn Wat. Engrs* **51**, 69.

U.S. Department of Health, Education and Welfare (1960). Transactions of seminar: "Algae and Metropolitan Wastes". Cincinnati, Ohio.

U.S. Department of Health, Education and Welfare (1964). "Influence of Impoundments on Water Quality", Cincinnati, Ohio.

Water Pollution Research (1962). Report of Water Pollution Research Board, p. 55.

Whitehead, R. C. (1948). Shustoke reservoir: biology and algal control. *J. Instn Wat. Engrs* **2**, 577.

Discussion

FORD: There is an increasing need for engineers concerned with lowland and estuarine design to ask biologists and chemists to study conditions which would pertain in severe droughts. The second, third and last paragraphs of Dr. Houghton's paper are especially valuable in this context. Biological effects usually assume greater importance in water supply reservoirs than in those for hydro-electric power and, in severe droughts, the former tend to be well drawn down. Thus dilution of inflowing polluted and/or productive river water is small and conditions could be such that the impounded water would deteriorate seriously in quality. Paradoxically, the growing tendency to require reservoirs to be designed also for recreational use should partly solve this problem by limitation of the permissible draw-down, although this usually involves extra cost. Severe draw-down of estuarine reservoirs might be precluded by the need to limit inward seepage of salt water, by amenity considerations or simply because capacity between higher levels would be adequate to maintain supplies during droughts.

The Multi-purpose Use of Reservoirs

LEONARD H. BROWN

Mid-Northamptonshire Water Board, Cliftonville, Northampton, England

Reservoirs may be made to conserve water for public water supply, for feeding water turbines to generate electricity, for industrial use, for irrigation of crops, for river regulation, for flood control or for other purposes. Some of these purposes may be combined. In addition, a reservoir built to conserve water may also be used for recreational purposes and it is on this aspect I propose to concentrate.

Where a reservoir is used to supply compensation water and not for public water supply, the activities are of less importance than if the reservoir is used for the supply of drinking water. When reservoirs were built for public water supply, it used to be the custom to surround them with strong fencing to keep out human beings. The removal of all possible sources of pollution, natural purification of water by storage and filtration through slow sand filters were the only means of providing people with a water supply, free from water-borne disease. The prevention of pollution necessitated keeping the gathering grounds free from human beings and also forbidding their access to the waters of the reservoirs. In modern times, with vastly improved methods of filtration, with chlorine, chloramine or ozone sterilization and with frequent laboratory checks on the quality of the water supplied, there is not the same necessity to keep people away from the raw waters, although pollution must still be guarded against. However, the access to reservoirs must be regarded as a privilege and not a right.

It cannot too often be emphasized that it is the first and most important duty of any water undertaker to provide for each and every consumer an adequate quantity of safe and suitable water or in the older phrase "pure and wholesome water". But it is usually possible to do this and at the same time to permit some of the general public to use the waters for recreation. Some waters are not filtered and especial care has to be taken to avoid pollution, but these cases are becoming rarer with the passage of time.

There is a growing demand from ratepayers that as they have helped to pay for the works they should be allowed to enjoy them.

With this in mind the Institution of Water Engineers set up a committee in 1962 to "consider and report upon the recreational use of water
works reservoirs of all kinds and the extent to which such reservoirs may
be used to the public advantage without detriment to the public water
supply". Their report was published in 1963, and may be obtained from
that Institution.

Fourteen activities were considered: (a) sailing; (b) fishing; (c) bird
watching; (d) shooting; (e) picnicking; (f) rock climbing; (g) rambling;
(h) water ski-ing; (i) public access to grounds around waterworks;
(j) recreational use of covered service reservoirs and water towers;
(k) rowing and canoeing; (l) swimming; (m) camping; (n) caravanning.

Sailing has become immensely popular in the last few years. After
being viewed with great suspicion by water undertakers, it is slowly gain-
ing approval. Three years ago six authorities permitted it and today the
number is not much greater. In suitable cases it is encouraged by the
Ministry of Education who may give grants towards the cost of suitable
club premises.

In order to control this sport it is generally agreed that a club should
manage the sailing and be responsible for the discipline of their members.
The Club's rules and by-laws should be subject to the approval of the
reservoir owner. One authority at least, insists on a thorough cleansing
and sterilization of the hull of any boat brought on to the water, whether
for the first time or after any period away.

Bacteriological analyses of raw water samples have not shown any
deterioration in the quality of the water due to sailing. The analyses of
the water in Pitsford reservoir, amongst others, have been carefully
watched, but there has never been any detectable increase in pollution
due to sailing.

Fishing is allowed nearly everywhere although the rules regulating the
conduct of the fishermen vary widely. With the same end in view, two
undertakers allow fishing from boats but prohibit it from the reservoir
shores, whereas three allow it from the shores but will not allow the use of
any boats. It is more common to permit both methods. As with sailing, management by a club is preferable to the selling of daily individual tickets.

Fishing need cause no deterioration in the quality of the water provided that the sanitary arrangements for the anglers are satisfactory and
provided that for a coarse fishery the more objectionable forms of bait
are not used.

Bird watching, shooting and rock climbing involve relatively few
people and can be limited and therefore controlled accordingly.

Other activities that might bring large numbers of people to reservoirs
are usually discouraged or prohibited.

All these things and others not yet mentioned give rise to arguments between the water undertaker and the organized bodies or individuals. The undertaker is concerned that at all times nothing should be done that will increase the risk of pollution. The visitors or would-be visitors will almost always argue that their particular type of activity will do no harm and alternatively that if it does then larger and better filters should be installed.

Let me quote from the report of the Institution of Water Engineers: "Theoretically the provision of public access to reservoir must inevitably result in an increased risk of pollution of that reservoir, the degree of risk being dependent upon the type of activity allowed and upon the precautions taken to minimize such pollution.

"Whether this increased risk has any practical significance or not depends upon the original quality of the water in the reservoir, the size of the reservoir in terms of the time during which the water is retained before passing into supply (in itself a purifying process), and the standard of treatment subsequently applied.

"In certain cases the increased risk will be found to have no practical significance, whereas in other cases it may be found to be totally unacceptable.

"The bacteriological quality of water in or drawn from a reservoir free from public access is governed by the following conditions:

Type of area of catchment

Activities on catchment, e.g. farming

Type and number of fauna on the catchment area

Birds resting on the reservoir, e.g. gulls

Storage, in terms of days' supply

Rainfall—seasonal variations and intensity

Temperature conditions and thermocline

Wind effects

"Type of water and its bacteriological productivity. Location of the outlet tower and depth of draw-off influencing the quality of water going to the treatment plant."

In addition to bacteriological pollution, the possibility of chemical pollution must not be overlooked.

What is certain is that the water undertaking should own and therefore control all the land on which their works are situated, together with the sporting rights.

In all cases the first essential is that proper sanitary accommodation and sewage disposal arrangements must be provided and properly maintained. This may or may not be easy; what is not easy is to persuade the visitor that these facilities are there to be used. Supervision is therefore essential. The amount of supervision will depend on the number of visitors, the area of the ground and the pattern of the behaviour of the youth in the neighbourhood.

The second requirement is to channel the casual visitor and small parties into areas set aside for them. Such areas need litter receptacles and car parking space. An enclosed area of some 10 acres was provided at Pitsford reservoir and has proved to be very popular and as a result another similar area may be provided there. Two areas have been provided at Diddington reservoir.

Where car parks are constructed a ditch should be dug along the side adjacent to the reservoir to minimize pollution and to stop any runaway vehicle.

There are many other requirements, particularly those intended either to secure the safety of the works or the safety of the visitor, or to secure the quiet enjoyment of the visitor by prohibiting noisy sports or the interference of one class of sport with another.

Finally in the Report of the Gathering Grounds Sub-Committee of the Central Advisory Water Committee there is this sentence: "We think it essential that any access permitted to a reservoir or its banks should always be treated as a valuable privilege and should only be permitted where the undertaker is satisfied, on solid grounds, that the privilege will not be abused."

Discussion

LOWENSTEIN: Does dumping old refuse in reservoirs present problems if you allow public access?

BROWN: Yes, old and stolen motor cars, for example, get dumped.

DREW: Speaking to the subject "multi-purpose use", it was surprising to have no mention of additional major (and often prior) justifications for barrage/dam/reservoir/lake construction, such as communications, navigation, flood control, irrigation etc. Mr. Brown commended "coming to terms" with recreational use, but even here he had clearly not taken the measure of demands which have, for example, just been stated publicly by the Chairman of the Northern Regional Planning Council, who called for the creation of substantial new recreational water areas *immediately* if the Lake District in particular is not to become entirely overwhelmed within the next ten years.

Mr. Brown's view is that "barrages are thirty years away" but we must recognize that whilst the full benefit from exploitation of the water potentials of a barrage proposition may only come in the longer term, there may be very significant and important *national* benefits—especially in relation to *communications* and *recreation* (which Mr. Brown admitted rapidly became self-supporting)—in, by virtually immediate construction, a location of high potential for a "demonstration project" such as the Solway.

BISWAS: As Mr. Brown's paper deals exclusively with only the recreational aspects of reservoirs, perhaps it would have been better entitled the "Recreational use of Reservoirs".

The focal point of much outdoor recreation is water and it is estimated that demand for outdoor recreation will treble by A.D. 2000 in the United States alone. Unlike irrigation, flood control, power or water supply, it is impossible to measure precisely the economic values of recreation in terms of money. No method has yet been devised to evaluate successfully human enjoyment, relaxation and determination of aesthetic values. Besides recreation, there is also a permanent economic benefit to the adjoining areas due to large public spending.

Sailing and water ski-ing have become increasingly popular within the last few years. This brings another problem, which is that accident claims can be very high. For one private concern with a lease agreement in Indianapolis for power-boating and allied facilities, under the terms of the concession the company has a public liability insurance of $1 000 000 for each accident, $200 000 for each person and $50 000 for each occurrence of property damage.

In the United Kingdom most of the projects seem to have been designed without much thought (if any) for the recreational purposes. This attitude could perhaps have been justified forty or fifty years ago on the ground that recreational water use could not be justified economically or there was not enough demand for it.

There is considerable controversy over the throwing open of reservoirs for recreational use. The American Water Works Association opposes any law demanding that recreational facilities be available in domestic water supply reservoirs and prefers the final say to be in the hands of the water control authorities. I am an advocate of recreational use of reservoirs if it can be achieved and feel that any successful hydraulic project must make complete economic use of every unit of land and water available. It is perfectly true that recreational use of impounded water will further increase the headache of the water authorities, but it must be remembered that without it life could be simpler but decidedly not better.

H

American Experience in Recreational Use of Artificial Waters

RICHARD H. STROUD

Sport Fishery Research Foundation and Sport Fishing Institute, Washington, D.C., U.S.A.

The U.S.A. has a maximum surface water resource embracing about 101·3 million acres. My concern today is with the roughly 13% that represents the man-made or artificial waters, or 13 million acres at maximum pool levels. In actual practice, it turns out to be somewhat less for purposes of fish production, effectively averaging about 10·2 million surface acres at average annual water levels.

Artificial waters ("man-made lakes") in the U.S.A. are referred to interchangeably as impoundments or reservoirs. Distinctions are made among (1) farm or ranch ponds (sometimes called "tanks" or stock tanks), generally those under 10 surface acres in area; (2) small reservoirs, from farm pond size up to 500 acres; and (3) large reservoirs, in excess of 500 acres (Jenkins, 1964), several of the largest approaching a half-million surface acres.

Numbering about 1·5 million units, farm ponds average about 0·8 surface acres. The remaining 9 million acres are composed of some 7·5 million acres of large reservoirs and about 1·5 million acres of small reservoirs. With the exception of 1 246 impoundments comprising 270 030 surface acres (including 1 234 small impoundments covering 206 840 acres, and twelve large impoundments including 63 190 acres), constructed specifically for recreational fishing (Stroud and Massmann, 1963), virtually all other impoundments were built for multiple-use purposes.

ROLE OF ANGLING IN AMERICAN RECREATION

The extent and nature of outdoor recreation was the object of a Congressionally-authorized $2·5 million three-year study by a temporary Outdoor Recreation Resources Review Commission. The study culminated in a monumental report to the President entitled "Outdoor Recreation in America" (Rockefeller et al., 1962). The report was based on the findings and implications of twenty-seven special investigations.

It confirmed that most outdoor recreation is centered around bodies of water, and that fishing is undoubtedly the most important form of water-based recreation. At least 46% of all Americans already utilize fishing as their principal means of outdoor recreation or wish to engage in it regularly. Its nearest rival in this respect is swimming (at something less than 50%, combined with "going to the beach"). These activities are followed in declining order of participation and interest by boating and canoeing (34%), camping (24%), hiking (22%), hunting (22%), and nature and bird walks (16%), with some other non-aquatic activities following. Significantly, the Commission found that up to 83% of all use of motorboats is for purposes of fishing (Leopold and Kinnison, 1962); that 75% of campers regard fishing as their principal reason for going camping (Mueller et al., 1962); and that over 75% of wilderness users include fishing among their objectives (being the major goal for one-third) during wilderness trips (Gilligan, 1962).

Obviously, fishing is a leading motivation to outdoor recreation participation in America. Indeed, the ORRRC study team analyzing participation in outdoor recreation, and the factors affecting outdoor recreation demand among American adults, found that fishing was exceeded in all mentions of leisure activity preference only by (1) looking at television, (2) reading, and (3) gardening, or working in the yard. Fishing exceeded "visiting with friends or relatives; participating in clubs, organizations, church work; spectator sports; playing cards; and going to movies." Conclusion (emphasis added): ". . . swimming, hunting, and *especially fishing* seem to be of the greatest importance and salience [in outdoor recreation]" (Mueller et al., 1962).

Within the total 1961 spectrum of U.S. outdoor recreation, fishing accounted for an estimated 560 million man-days. This compared to 760 million man-days of swimming, 480 million man-days of picnicking, 260 million man-days of boating, 240 million man-days of hunting, and 50 million man-days of water ski-ing (Ferriss et al., 1962). About 26% of annual fishing activity (man-days) occurred in the spring, 47% in summer, 18% in fall, and 9% in winter. Virtually all water ski-ing is done during the warm months; even so, during summer, anglers outnumber water-skiers by 6 to 1. During the fall months, a time of concentration on hunting, fishing activity (100 million man-days) also managed to outrank hunting activity (97 million man-days), if narrowly!

EXTENT OF RESERVOIR FISHING

With respect to man-made lakes, about 1 200 large impoundments now provide about one-third of the surface acreage (at average levels) making up U.S. inland waters available for public fishing, exclusive of Alaska and the Great Lakes. According to a special ORRRC sport fishing study, sponsored by the Outdoor Recreation Resources Review Commission (King *et al.*, 1962), warmwater species predominate in 85% of productive public impoundments, and coldwater species in the remaining 15%. On the basis of reports from thirty-one states, average angler harvests from large reservoirs in 1960 were about 15·7 lb per acre at warmwater reservoirs and 9·0 lb at coldwater reservoirs. Nationally, the sport catch per angler-day in major reservoirs averaged approximately 1·1 lb in coldwater reservoirs and 1·5 lb in warmwater reservoirs.

Total 1963 fishing effort was estimated at 86 million days on large public reservoirs, equivalent to about 10 man-days per acre, thereby comprising one-quarter of all angling effort on inland fresh waters (Jenkins, 1964). By 1976, large reservoirs (including new construction) were expected to experience an 85% increase in angling, a jump of 75 million man-days in the ensuing 13 years. To maintain fishing success near the present level, warmwater fish creeled from reservoirs must be increased 30% from the 1960 estimated average of 15·7 lb per acre to 21 lb in 1976. To meet an estimated 1976 demand for 161 million man-days of angling (King *et al.*, 1962), a 30% increase in yield (through improved management) must be combined with the construction of 5 million acres of new impoundments (expected to be realized from current authorizations).

FARM PONDS

A surprising amount of fishing is afforded by farm ponds. A detailed analysis was made of the fishing in a random sample of 1 000 ponds, from among 200 000 farm ponds stocked by the U.S. Fish and Wildlife Service between 1953 and 1957. This led to the estimate that at least five million persons (about 11% of all U.S. anglers) found 20 million man-days of recreational fishing (nearly 4% of all angling, nationwide) at farm pond waters in 1959 (King, 1960). The study revealed that 21% of the pond owners had added fish of their own, and that 30% of the ponds contained wild fish. In the 15% of ponds where fishing was unsatisfactory, the more common causes were: (a) too many small bluegills, (b) muddy water, and (c) presence of wild fish.

The normal species combination and original stocking ratios employed in the majority of farm pond fish management ventures involve centrarchids, generally largemouth bass, *Micropterus salmoides*, bluegills and/or redear sunfish, *Lepomis machrochirus* and *L. microlophus* (Swingle and Smith, 1947); or, as now being tried increasingly, channel catfish, *Ictalurus punctatus* (Prather, 1964a,b), tilapia, *Tilapia mossambica*

(McConnell, 1965), or rainbow trout, *Salmo gairdneri* (Eipper, 1960). The basic principles of fish population dynamics enunciated at Auburn University (Alabama) during two decades of experimental research on warmwater species combinations (Swingle, 1950), have been successfully applied during the past decade to twenty state-owned small reservoirs throughout Alabama (Byrd and Crance, 1965).

SMALL RESERVOIRS

The smallest of the Alabama lakes is 32 acres, the largest is 250 acres, averaging 87 acres, totalling 1 733 acres; six are 100 acres or larger. The system has been characterized by sustained high yields during the 15-year history of the expanding community lakes program. Only two of the lakes are less than 5 years old, six are 5–10 years old, and twelve are now 10–15 years old. Average annual catches, principally largemouth bass, bluegills and redear sunfish, aggregated 573 fish weighing 173 lb per acre (including thirty largemouth bass weighing 29 lb) during 135 angler-days of fishing per acre of water surface per year. Altogether, 1 844 397 recorded fishermen caught 7 855 325 fish weighing 2 375 788 lb during the first 14 years. The totals included 413 876 largemouth bass weighing 395 222 lb (5·3% of number, 16·7% of weight).

From the outset, these bass-bluegill lakes have been open to continuous year-round fishing, without minimum size limits. The long-term catch records show that year-round fishing has not been correlated, at least in those waters, with any consistent trend toward decreasing average size of the species caught—as is occasionally suggested by some American sports writers. Rather, average sizes of bass and bream caught there are known to have varied up and down principally with respect to other factors, especially year-class strength.

The Alabama program is an outstanding long-term record of solid accomplishment in providing recreational fishing where comparatively little existed previously. Throughout the U.S., by 1964, a total of 1 231 similar community fishing lakes had been created by state fish conservation agencies in forty-five states.* These small reservoirs, comprising 197 840 surface acres, average about 160 acres. Not all such lakes receive the same intensive level of management as those in Alabama, nor always support as many fishing trips per acre annually. Nevertheless, most of them support several times as much fishing as do unmanaged or extensively managed natural lakes; generally, they are known to support 100 or more man-days of angling per acre annually.

*In addition, small reservoirs constructed with tribal funds by Indians, to provide trout fishing by daily fee to anglers from outside the reservations, well managed, are successful business enterprises.

Most of these lakes are managed exclusively for fishing; i.e. water ski-ing and use of high-powered boats are generally prohibited, and swimming is often excluded. At the same time, other recreation is often encouraged on surrounding lands that may be acquired by local governmental agencies and developed as parkland. An outstanding example of this is 215-acre Burke Lake, constructed by the Virginia Game and Inland Fisheries Commission, about 25 miles southwest of Washington, D.C. It was conceived as a cooperative multiple-use project with the Fairfax County Park Authority, which developed camping, picnicking, and related activities on 532 acres it acquired adjacent to the lake. During the first full season of operation (1 December, 1963 to 30 November 1964), the Authority reported that person-visits to Burke Lake totalled 190 767. At least half (over 95 000) were for the purpose of fishing; a corresponding number were for picnicking, bird watching, and camping. There were 440 fishing trips per acre of water surface (Stroud, 1965).

In a progress report to the Commission, Virginia's able fishery chief came to this conclusion: "Without question Burke Lake has received the highest usage of any of the 16 Commission constructed lakes. A great deal of the credit for this should be given the 'multiple use concept' associated with the development of related outdoor recreational activities by the Park Authority on lands around the lake. Fishing and these other activities were complementary and no use friction was apparent. More fishing was done by family groups at Burke than at other Commission facilities. Future public fishing lake development by the Commission should be guided by this example, with every emphasis placed on entering into similar agreements with other public agencies entrusted with providing outdoor recreation."

LARGE RESERVOIRS

True multiple recreational use of large reservoirs has become evident in America only since World War II. The large man-made lakes are constructed, with few exceptions, for purpose others than recreation (generally for hydroelectric generation, flood control, navigation, or a combination of these). The vast majority of the 1 200 large multi-purpose impoundments, totalling some 7·5 million acres at average annual levels, have been constructed by the U.S. Army Corps of Engineers, the U.S. Bureau of Reclamation, various municipalities, and various large public and private utilities and other industry. Multiple use of these waters for recreation has generally been a grudging and reluctant accommodation, at least until the last decade. Significant change in the national attitude, dating from about 1955, was greatly accelerated by the 1959–62 activities and Report of the Outdoor Recreation Resources Review Commission (Rockefeller *et al.*, 1962).

The problem of changing attitude toward multiple use of reservoirs is nowhere better illustrated than in the case of municipal water supplies. A recent study on 700-acre Forrest Lake, a water supply reservoir serving the domestic needs of Kirksville, Missouri (population 13 300), proved beyond question that a broad spectrum of recreational activities there (among the most intensive known on a domestic water supply) did not endanger the public's health through impairment of its drinking water (Rosebery, 1964).

During the 3-year period, 1958–60, an average of 291 000 people visited Forrest Lake annually. During the summer months, about 22% were sightseeing, 19% picnicking, 16% swimming, 14% fishing, 11% boating, 6% camping, and 4% water ski-ing (the remaining 8% were unclassified). There were over 40 000 swimmer-days each year. From 700 to 750 boats were licensed to operate on the reservoir each year. Almost 90% of the anglers fished from boats—and caught an average of one fish every 46 min.

This intensive recreational use had little effect upon water quality at the intake tower of the water filtration plant. Sampling of coliform and enterococcus bacteria with the membrane filter method revealed relatively low densities. Highest counts were noted below the thermocline, and in a cove receiving heavy use from boats, wave action, drainage from a camping area, and seepage from the park sewage septic tank. It was concluded that the existing condition of pollution in Forrest Lake would need to increase considerably before there would be additional costs for filtration and purification of the municipal water supply.

The desirability of using domestic water supplies for fishing and other recreational purposes is being demonstrated repeatedly. More and more industrial and municipal impoundments are opened to fishing each year, especially near urban centers. The fact that recreational activities on drinking water supplies do not endanger the public is being recognized by an increasing number of responsible public health officials. In a report to Congress on environmental health, for example, the U.S. Surgeon General stated, in part (Burney, 1960; emphasis added):

> In community planning, requirements for recreation areas and their relationship to community living as a whole are matters of concern to health personnel. For example *the use of domestic water supply reservoirs for fishing and other recreational purposes is feasible* if the public is willing to pay the price of necessary protection. Thus, the interplay of several elements of environmental health is demonstrated once again.

Opening of domestic water supplies to public fishing is often at least partly the result of much persuasion, consultation, and cooperation in fish management by the state fishery agencies. For example, a survey of the administration of 163 Texas water supply reservoirs revealed that fishing was permitted on 89% of them (Bonn, 1963). The information from the ninety-seven agencies controlling these reservoirs (up to 20 000 surface acres), indicated that closures to fishing, where they occurred, were due either to lack of adequate filtering systems or to the lake being too small to permit a restricted zone near the water intake. In addition to fishing, picnicking was allowed at 67% of the impoundments, boating at 60%, camping at 44%, hunting at 42%, water ski-ing at 37%, and swimming at 28%. In a talk before the Texas Water and Sewage Works Association, the survey author (a Texas Game and Fish Commission biologist) noted:

> Some cities do not want to get into the "fishing business". But few are the cities today that do not provide parks, playgrounds, stadiums and other places for the recreation and relaxation of their citizens. Fishing is also a recreation, so why not provide a place for it too?

A nationwide survey, conducted by the Sport Fishing Institute, revealed that at least 93% of all municipal reservoirs reported had been opened to public fishing by 1960. Over 362 000 acres of industrial and 1 080 000 acres of municipal water supply reservoirs were recorded in this category. Reports from the individual states revealed that the majority of water supplies were closed to recreational fishing in only six of the fifty states (Connecticut, Hawaii, Massachusetts, Montana, Pennsylvania, and Rhode Island; Stroud, 1963).

Problems Associated with Recreational Use

The central problem with respect to recreational use of American reservoirs, especially fishing, has three prongs, namely: (1) inadequate access to permit full use of reservoir fishery resources; (2) conflicts arising over competing recreational use of the water surface by various boating activities; and (3) inadequate knowledge of reservoir ecology to provide the needed springboard for improved management of fish populations required to sustain or restore good sport fishing.

ASSURING PUBLIC ACCESS

One of the important innovations in U.S. fishery administration following World War II arose from these dual realizations: (1) creation of good fishing would be to little avail unless there is permanently assured means of public access to the publicly owned fishery resources, and (2) this could no longer be taken for granted. It had already become

H*

obvious that many waters were overcrowded with anglers while other
waters went quite unused because there was no way to reach them.
Consequently, the state fish and game agencies, and the federal reservoir
construction agencies as well, had already initiated significant public
access programs by the time the Outdoor Recreation Resources Review
Commission in due course confirmed the fundamental importance to
fishing, particularly to boat-fishing, of adequate access to recreational
waters. The Commission predicted that the amount of fishing in the
year 2000 will be three times what it was in 1960. It is believed that the
facility needs of this increased fishing demand can be satisfactorily met,
provided, among other requirements, that existing waters, both fresh and
salt, and the expected new impoundments, will have been made accessible to public use. The Commission secured data on the extent of waters
already entirely closed to public fishing (or subject to arbitrary closure
at any time). Among them, nearly 1 million acres of large public reservoirs
were wholly inaccessible and much of 7 million acres were poorly accessible (King *et al.*, 1962).

At an average suggested ratio of one 10-acre site per 500 acres of water,
the equivalent of 2 000 10-acre sites would be needed for the inaccessible
waters alone. Recent costs of acquisition and development (Stroud and
Massmann, 1963) indicate that at least $14·4 million would be required
to meet these barely minimal needs, with up to $100 million or more
required for provision of full access to all reservoirs for sport fishing,
alone. Obviously, the aquatic recreationists must contribute their fair
share of the burden for cost of these vital multiple-benefit facilities,
directly or indirectly. The task of meeting the need at federally constructed reservoirs, especially those built by the U.S. Army Corps of Engineers,
is well under way through Congressional appropriations to the construction agencies out of general funds, recreation having become accepted as
a project purpose. By 1964, annual appropriations had reached over $11
million for access site development at Corps reservoirs, both completed
and under construction.

WATER-USE CONFLICTS

Intimately associated with development of access to fishing waters is
the parallel growth of acute problems of recreational water conflicts,
especially between anglers on the one hand, whether fishing from boats
or from shore, and speed boaters and water skiers on the other hand.
Up until a decade ago, when the situation underwent drastic change,
the nation's multi-million angler army had the nation's waterways
pretty much to themselves so far as boat traffic was concerned. By 1960,
however, water skiers probably numbered two to three million or more.

Associated with water ski-ing are high speeds of boat operation and youthful age of operators, as well as a need for large areas of unobstructed water for pursuit of this activity.

Some 40–50% of American anglers now use boats of some kind for fishing, with over 80% of boat use devoted to the fishing activity. Use of boats for sport fishing is often the most practical means of getting at fish populations. This is especially true at large reservoirs where from under half to over 90% of all fishing may be done from boats. At Oklahoma's 19 000-acre Fort Gibson reservoir in 1955 and 1956, about 40% of nearly 600 000 angler-days of annual fishing effort was carried on from boats. A census of the fishing revealed that water-use conflicts had developed there to serious proportions in the space of but two seasons. Speed boat racing and water ski-ing in certain areas of the reservoir had produced "intolerable disturbance" to many anglers. It was noted that fishing effort during the second summer of the census, when this condition developed, decreased decidedly from that experienced the previous summer (Houser and Heard, 1957).

The Outdoor Recreation Resources Review Commission research team studying recreational fishing surveyed the state fishery agencies as to the degree of competition for use of public waters that existed in 1961 between anglers and water skiers and speed boat operators. Twelve states rated the competition as "severe", twenty-four states as "moderate", and twelve as "slight". Among these, thirty-five states had taken some kind of action to regulate conflicts of interest.

Many local efforts have been made to develop solutions that will permit *reasonable* accommodation of the newer minority water sports, while not penalizing unduly the traditional majority rights of anglers to fish relatively undisturbed. A useful pattern seems to be emerging, involving some form of zoning, either in terms of space (area) or in terms of time (hours, days) or some possible combination of these. In any event, the Outdoor Recreation Resources Review Commission stated in its Report (Rockefeller *et al.*, 1962) to the President and the Congress (emphasis added):

> Public action is needed to resolve conflicts between recreation and other uses of water *as well as among recreation activities themselves.*

Relative to the latter consideration, the Commission said further, in part:

> The use of such a device as activity zoning can do much to resolve these problems. Unless prompt action is taken, however, dangerous conditions will become even worse, as the demand for water-related outdoor recreation continues to climb.

EXPANDING THE SCIENTIFIC BASE

It is widely recognized that the anticipated future fishing demands cannot be accommodated unless an increase in the yield of sport fishes can be achieved through improvement in fish management practices. It is not to be inferred, however, that much useful information is lacking. On the contrary, a great deal has been accomplished since the close of World War II, especially with respect to the liberalization of arbitrarily restrictive fishing regulations. The now widespread practice of year-round fishing for warmwater fish was conceived as a result of ecological research conducted during the 1940's on the large multi-purpose reservoirs of the Tennessee Valley Authority.

I have already discussed the successful application of this practice to the small reservoirs of Alabama. The first application, however, occurred in 1944 at TVA's 34 000-acre Norris reservoir, Tennessee, continuously applied thereafter. Two decades later, in 1963, the huge TVA lake supported some 312 000 angler-days of fishing—more than double the 140 000 angler-days experienced during 1944. Year-round fishing has continued to serve usefully by making many more recreational fishing days available to anglers than are possible with closed seasons, without demonstrable harmful effects upon the fish population (Stroud, 1964). By 1963, the practice had received extensive application in forty-five states (Stroud and Massmann, 1963).

Much more could be said on the vitally important subject of reservoir research. However, this would more profitably await the results of some of the important ecological research now in progress under the recently established National Reservoir Research Program of the U.S. Fish and Wildlife Service (Jenkins, 1964). Suffice it, now, to predict that it will become possible in the next few decades to manage many large impoundments for improved yields of desired species of game fishes.

Over the past decade, in the U.S.A., much has been written about various problems associated with the recreational use of man-made lakes. Nevertheless, I shall refrain from further discussion of them. Instead, I cite two elements that contribute strongly to good fishing in America in addition to requisite bountiful natural resources. America's 60 million anglers, particularly the 34 million who make up the confirmed hard-core of the angling fraternity, are generally conservation-oriented —if sometimes misinformed and occasionally ill-advised in their actions. Considerable progress has been made in fish conservation, including the vital matter of water pollution control, no little portion of it because of the constructive attitude by informed national conservation leaders backed by the militant support of this great army of fishermen.

I also wish to give credit to the American fishing tackle manufacturing industry for its financial and vocal support of fish conservation through the organization that I am privileged to head, the Sport Fishing Institute. Since 1950, also, the industry has supported a 10% excise tax on certain of its own products. Moreover, in concert with its customers, the anglers, the industry successfully fought to *retain* the tax in the face of the general effort to eliminate or reduce all excise taxes formerly levied on a host of manufactured items. Why did fishing tackle manufacturers take exception to the general trend? Because the tackle excise tax is a significant source of supplemental funding for the state fishery agencies to use in spearheading their biological research, fish population manipulation, and facilities acquisition and development activities. These are the vital modern activities necessary to creation of needed good fishing for about 60 million anglers.

REFERENCES

Bonn, E. (1963). Plan for leisure. *Tex. Game Fish* **21**(2), 18–19.
Burney, L. E. (1960). The Surgeon General's report to the House Committee on Appropriations, Public Health Service, Department of Health, Education and Welfare, January 1960. In "Report on Environmental Health Problems: 4–33. Hearings Before the Subcommittee of the Committee on Appropriations, House of Representatives, 86th Congress, 2nd Session." U.S. Government Printing Office, Washington, D.C.
Byrd, I. B. and Crance, J. H. (1965). Fourteen years of management and fishing success in Alabama's state-owned public fishing lakes. *Trans. Am. Fish. Soc.* **94**(2), 129–134.
Eipper, A. W. (1960). Managing farm ponds for trout production. *Cornell Ext. Bull.* 1036, 31 pp.
Ferriss, A. L., Churchill, B. C., Proctor, C. H. and Zazove, L. E. H. (1962). National recreation survey. Outdoor Recreation Resources Review Commission; ORRRC Study Report 19, 390 pp. U.S. Government Printing Office, Washington, D.C.
Gilligan, J. P., Ed. (1962). Wilderness and recreation—a report on resources, values and problems. Outdoor Recreation Resources Review Commission; ORRRC Study Report 3, 352 pp. U.S. Government Printing Office, Washington, D.C.
Houser, A. and Heard, W. R. (1957). A one-year creel-census on Fort Gibson Reservoir. *Proc. Okla. Acad. Sci.* 38 137–146.
Jenkins, R. M. (1964). Reservoir fishery research strategy and tactics. Fish and Wildlife Circ. 196, 12 pp. U.S. Government Printing Office, Washington, D.C.
King, W. (1960). A survey of fishing in 1 000 ponds in 1959. Fish and Wildlife Circ. 86, 20 pp. U.S. Government Printing Office, Washington, D.C.
King, W., Hemphill, J., Swartz, A. and Stutzman, K. (1962). Sport fishing—today and tomorrow. Outdoor Recreation Resources Review Commission; ORRRC Study Report 7, 119 pp. U.S. Government Printing Office, Washington, D.C.

Leopold, L. B. and Kinnison, H. B. (1962). Water for recreation—values and opportunities. Outdoor Recreation Resources Review Commission; ORRRC Study Report 10, 73 pp. U.S. Government Printing Office, Washington, D.C.

McConnell, W. J. (1965). *Tilapia*, a fish for ranch ponds. *Prog. Agric. Ariz.* **17**(2), 3–4.

Mueller, E., Gurin, G. and Wood M. (1962). Participation in outdoor recreation: factors affecting demand among American adults. Outdoor Recreation Resources Review Commission; ORRRC Study Report 20, 94 pp. U.S. Government Printing Office, Washington, D.C.

Prather, E. E. (1964a). Experiments with white catfish as a sport fish. (Ms.). Agric. Expt. Stn, Auburn Univ., Auburn, Ala.

Prather, E. E. (1964b). Experiments on the use of channel catfish as sport fish. (Ms.). Agric. Expt. Stn, Auburn Univ., Auburn, Ala.

Rockefeller, L. S., *et al.* (1962). Outdoor Recreation for America. Outdoor Recreation Resources Review Commission Report. 245 pp. U.S. Government Printing Office, Washington, D.C.

Roseberry, D. A. (1964). Relationship of recreational use of Forrest Lake and bacterial densities. *J. Am. Wat. Wrks Ass.* **56**(1), 43–59.

Stroud, R. H. (1963). Fish conservation. *In* "The Fisherman's Encyclopedia," pp. 329–413 (rev. ed.). The Stackpole Co., Harrisburg, Pa.

Stroud, R. H. (1964). Liberalized fishing at Norris. *Sport Fish. Inst. Bull.* **157**, 4–5.

Stroud, R. H. (1965). County recreation leadership. *Sport Fish. Inst. Bull.* **159**, 1.

Stroud, R. H. and Massmann, W. H. (1963). Fish Conservation Highlights, 1960–1962. 84 pp. Sport Fishing Institute, Washington, D.C.

Swingle, H. S. (1950). Relationships and dynamics of balanced and unbalanced fish populations. Bull. 274 (73 pp.), Agric. Exp. Stn, Auburn Univ., Auburn, Ala.

Swingle, H. S. and Smith, E. V. (1947). Management of farm fish ponds. Bull. 254 (30 pp.), Agric. Exp. Stn, Auburn Univ., Auburn, Ala.

Discussion

OLIVER: Are the Alabama lakes natural or are they stocked?

STROUD: They are mostly dams on rivers. Rotenone is used, then they are stocked once only. After this the fish stocks keep up naturally, unless something like a road construction accident happens. But the lakes are fertilized; there is intensive management.

General Discussion

ATKINSON-WILLES: Another aspect of the multi-purpose use of reservoirs is their value in the conservation of migratory water birds. Wildfowl in particular are subject to considerable human pressure, one of the greatest threats being the loss of natural habitat through land drainage and reclamation. Offsetting this loss are the big new reservoirs, which in recent winters have been attracting an appreciable proportion of the migratory population. Sixteen of these man-made lakes, all lowland and mostly lying in southern and eastern England, are especially valuable to wildfowl; together they hold an estimated 3% of the mallard population in England, Scotland and Wales, 4% of the teal and wigeon, and as much as 15–20% of the pochard and tufted ducks (Atkinson-Willes, Ed. (1963) Nature Conservancy Monograph No. 3. H.M.S.O., London).

Until recently most reservoirs could be regarded as virtual sanctuaries by reason of the strict control on public access; now an increasing number of water engineers are prepared to afford facilities to approved recreations, such as sailing and fishing, which to a greater or lesser extent are incompatible with wildfowl interests. Unfortunately, the demand for recreational facilities is often heaviest on the reservoirs most used by ducks. Some compromise is therefore needed to ensure that wildfowl are allotted a fair share of the available water space. Having already been deprived of much of their natural habitat, they must not be denied the use of the man-made lakes on which they have come to rely.

BROWN: The largest reservoir in our area is 850 acres. We are restraining sailors to the lower end and the top half is being kept as a nature reserve.

WHITE: I would like to raise the question of the Wash Lake, the biological implications, likely water quality, and cost. I expect that in some ways we would have the same conditions in the Wash as in Solway and Morecambe Bay, but in some respects they would be different. We have no problems of sport fishing in the salmon and trout sense, although we are interested in commercial fishing, and we are involved in the improvement of shipping and navigation facilities.

The exact position of the dam has not been determined, but the area enclosed could be from 150 000 to 200 000 acres (say nearly 400 sq. miles), so that it would be around eight or ten times as big as Morecambe. The depth may average 30 ft, with much deeper pools in places. Storage capacity would, I understand, be from 1 to 1½ million million gal. Capital investment would be large, but would be likely to represent good value in view of the vast quantity of water stored. Perhaps this large size, with its effect on such influences as wave action, oxygenation, and length of storage, would give the Wash Lake special advantages so far as the quality of water is concerned. Would Mr. Law comment on the scheme?

LAW: I regret that I cannot give any details of the Wash scheme—I know it to be a gigantic project, but do not know the estimated costs or capacities. A snag about the Wash barrage is the amount of sewage effluent going into the rivers draining into it—to use the Wash for storage would mean the recirculation of these sewage effluents many more times. If such a barrage were constructed, it might be worthwhile to pipe water thereto from the North of England so that when water was plentiful in the north it could be used to dilute the sewage effluents in the Wash. It should also be remembered that quite frequently the weather in the south-east is different from that in the north-west—one area might be experiencing a drought whilst in the other the rainfall was normal, or even above the average, and a large spinal water grid might then be very useful.

FISH: I wish to repudiate what I can only describe as "loose talk" regarding the quality of the surface waters in south-east England. The river waters are not polluted and are not dirty. They may contain high proportions of effluent but persons like Dr. Houghton do an excellent job in treating these waters, drawn from near the tidal limits of the rivers, to produce perfectly satisfactory public water supplies.

In other parts of the country, efforts need to be made on water conservation grounds to do the same as in south-east England, namely making use of water derived from the lower reaches of rivers and thereby re-using the effluents those waters contain.

HOUGHTON: I fully agree with Mr. Fish that the Essex river water is carefully looked after and compares well in quality with that elsewhere in the country. Under ordinary flow conditions at present there is no trouble, but one has to consider the position in extreme drought, especially as the flow of effluent is continually increasing. An important point is whether the abstraction of river water leads to more than one re-use of effluent before it finally reaches the tide-way; where effluent is re-used in Essex most of it does not have more than one re-use. If there is successive recycling of effluent through a conventional water treatment works a build-up of impurities may occur. There was, in fact, a published account of such a recycling at Chanute in Kansas some years ago. While there was no obvious deterioration in the health of the community much difficulty was experienced, for instance, on account of high detergent content causing foaming.

LITTLE: Purified water is wasted on washing cars, toilets etc., and very little gets drunk. In U.S.A. one can buy a de-ionizing water gadget to make tasteless water. Would it be sensible to filter our own drinking water and use other water not so carefully prepared for other things?

HOUGHTON: I do not think it would be practical to rely on people purifying their own drinking water and there would also be much general risk to hygiene in a public supply of impure water for purposes other than drinking.

Addendum

Comments on the Symposium in the Light of the
Biology of U.S. Reservoirs

RICHARD H. STROUD

*Sport Fishery Research Foundation and Sport Fishing Institute,
Washington, D.C., U.S.A.*

The foregoing discussion of tropical reservoirs and the Africa Science Board's bibliography entitled "Man-made Lakes: A Selected Guide to the Literature" (National Academy of Science-National Research Council, Washington, D.C.) have both given too little cognizance to temperate zone reservoir research. Such work has revealed much of a fundamental nature about the biological and limnological principles of reservoir regimes that should be at least broadly applicable to problems in tropical areas.

If the deficiency is due partly to lack of awareness of the American literature or to lack of its ready availability, the recent release of the comprehensive "Bibliography on Reservoir Fishery Biology in North America", compiled by Robert M. Jenkins, Director, National Reservoir Research Program, U.S. Fish and Wildlife Service, helps to resolve the problem (U.S. Bureau of Sport Fisheries and Wildlife Research Report 68, available from the Bureau, Washington, D.C.).

There are now some 1 200 large reservoirs (7·5 million acres) in the U.S. The National Reservoir Research Program has thus far assembled and catalogued data on some 640 of these large reservoirs, including up to thirty-eight parameters describing associated environmental factors. Arrangements have been completed for computer programming and use of an IBM 7040 computer in multivariate analyses of factors influencing reservoir fish production. A significant number of these large reservoirs have been studied extensively and intensively in the past ten to thirty years.

United States federal law, recently strengthened in this respect, has required for nearly two decades that the effects of engineering schemes upon fishery (and wildlife) resources be studied and recommendations made for mitigation of losses, or enhancement of resources (recent). Thus, U.S. experience can provide a partial answer to the unanswered question of yesterday, viz: "What length of lead-time must biologists

205

have in order to advise engineers on measures required to accommodate the needs of fishery resources?'' In the U.S.A., at least three years are considered necessary for actual preimpoundment surveys and related research plus a minimum of two years for programming the work (assuming no delays in provision of requisite funding), or a total five-year lead-time over commencement of design engineering.

Invariably, the initial worrisome limnological pattern of tropical reservoirs has also characterized the first few years of impoundment in U.S. reservoirs. However, improvement often occurs thereafter. Thus, for three to five years, there characteristically is an extinction of dissolved oxygen in the hypolimnion, and distinct chemical as well as thermal stratification. These conditions become modified favorably to a greater or lesser extent in following years. U.S. experience has shown rather clearly that the extent to which this improvement obtains is largely a function of the vertical location of the penstock intake openings, relative to (1) the maximum depth of the reservoir at the dam and (2) the total volume of the hypolimnial water in comparison to later flow release schedules for power generation, etc.

Here, then, is a significant example where the recommendations of biologists can provide helpful guidance to engineers. This is another partial answer to a second engineering plea that was left essentially unanswered yesterday.

Superior fisheries are expected to develop in U.S. reservoirs (in the absence of anadromous fishery complications) where the dams are constructed with ample height and provided with low elevation penstock intakes. This permits planned water releases to be withdrawn well below the thermocline so as to exhaust annually large fractions of the hypolimnion. Otherwise, with penstock intakes at thermocline depth or shallower, much of the potential reservoir fish production becomes irreversibly foreclosed by committing the hypolimnion to indefinite stagnation. It has proven comparatively easy to reconstitute fish populations in accommodation of drastic changes in downstream ecology resulting from a regime of hypolimnial water releases below dams. Overlooking the opportunity to fix the future limnology of the reservoir along favorable lines, through preoccupation with efforts to preserve the original ecology of remaining downstream sections, can fatally preclude optimum utilization of the future reservoir.

Declining reservoir productivity with increasing reservoir age has often been claimed in the U.S.A. Yet, it seems that this may well be a misinterpretation of the evidence (at least for reservoirs having hypolimnial water releases), in terms of fish end-products. For example, Joeris indicated that fish are probably more abundant in Kariba now, in spite of

recent declines in commercial fish harvests that were cited as indicative
of declining productivity. Joeris stated that improved limnological conditions in Kariba have resulted in a greater depth range utilization by
fish populations, which results in increased utilization of bottom area,
thereby *increasing* production. A quick calculation that I made on the
basis of figures cited yesterday revealed that less than 1/100 lb per acre
of fish are being harvested from Kariba—scarcely overexploitation.
Obviously, chief concern should be on methods to increase commercial
fish harvests plus encouragement of sport fishing.

What really happens, with increasing age of U.S. reservoirs, is that
"rough" fishes increase at the expense of game fishes (many of which,
being nest-builders, are more inhibited by uncontrolled fluctuations in
water levels, or adversely affected by increased turbidity caused by
feeding habits of rough fishes, etc.). During the initial year or two of
impoundment, game fish reproduction is highly successful in the expanding new environment with its relative lack of significant competition
for food and space. After filling, early reservoir conditions become more
conducive to successful reproduction of competitor species and relatively
less favorable to game species.

Nearly a decade ago, Jenkins showed that *total weight* of fish present
(standing crop) in a series of small Oklahoma reservoirs gradually increased with increasing duration of impoundment and progressive accumulation of bottom sediments and nutrients (Jenkins, R. M. The standing
crop of fish in Oklahoma ponds. *Proc. Okla. Acad. Sci.* (1957) **38** 157–
172). The work on drastic reservoir drawdowns by Bennett at the Illinois
Natural History Survey has shown that the expanding-environment
phenomenon can be induced artificially in man-made lakes as often as
desired (Bennett, G. W. (1962). "Management of Artificial Lakes and
Ponds". Reinhold, New York, and Chapman and Hall, London). Too,
it was over twenty years ago that TVA fishery biologists demonstrated
the value of controlling water-levels for enhancement of reproduction
by centrarchid fishes, and secured beneficial modifications in flow release
schedules by TVA engineers for this purpose.

The burden of evidence is that reservoir productivity increases rather
than decreases with aging of the reservoir. Unfortunately, this fact is
often obscured by exclusive dependence on yield analysis, due to
changing composition and/or behavior of the fish populations, or through
overconcentration on classical limnological research. Biological investigations (especially of fish populations) are vitally necessary for adequate
understanding of reservoir ecology. For example, sport fish yields from
10 000-acre Hiwassee reservoir in North Carolina were much lower per
unit of surface than at 34 000-acre Norris reservoir in Tennessee.

Detailed examination revealed close biological, chemical and hydrologic similarity between them, with one notable exception. Hiwassee lacked a pelagic forage fish for conversion of plankton to fish. A plankton-feeding pelagic species (*Dorosoma cepedianum*) was introduced and game fish production and sport fish yields improved substantially following its establishment in the biota. There are many similar examples of the beneficial application of this principle to reservoirs throughout the United States.

Mention has been made of increased fish production associated with improvements in water quality, with respect to Kariba. Prior temperate zone experience suggests that this can often be expected, perhaps aided. For example, Norris reservoir, a large deep storage reservoir in the TVA system, was closed in 1936. It filled within one year, although five years had been the anticipated filling time. A pronounced dissolved oxygen deficiency characterized the hypolimnial waters during the first three years or so, below a pronounced thermocline. Thereafter, a gradual progressive improvement in water quality occurred. By the end of the first decade, oxygen-deficient density currents were charted half way down the reservoir whereas, earlier, they had extended to the dam. From the outset, reasonably good fishing prevailed for the warmwater Centrarchidae in the epilimnion and thermocline. In the 1940's, gill-net samples yielded substantial catches of Percidae (*Stizostedion vitreum* and *S. canadense*) as well, both within and below the oxygen-deficient density currents, and these fishes were significant in the angling catches. In the 1950's, the density currents were much less conspicuous, and fishing was excellent. By the 1960's, oxygen-deficient density currents rarely occurred, and the hypolimnial waters remained sufficiently well oxygenated so that rainbow trout could be introduced to utilize this new biological niche and supplement the production of the other fishes. Yields of the latter had also increased substantially over former years.

In conclusion, it appears to me that the understanding of tropical reservoir problems would be accelerated by full appreciation of the considerable research that has been accomplished on temperate zone reservoirs. I submit that the broad principles (if not the local details), that have been revealed therefrom concerning the dynamics of reservoir ecology, have wide applicability. By taking full advantage of this relatively untapped pool of information, much helpful advice can be given to engineers decades earlier than would otherwise be possible. Thus, increased benefits would be secured to the under-developed nations from reservoir construction through better informed biological advice.

Author Index

(Numbers in italics refer to the References at the end of each article.)

A

Allanson, B. R., 63, *68*
Allsopp, W. H. L., 82, *84*
Amarteifio, G. W., 102, *108*
Andrew, F. J., 56, *68*

B

Bailey, M., 132, *135*
Bailey, R. G., 58, *68*
Bakker, C., 124, *127*
Balinsky, B. I., 59, *68*
Baxter, G., 165, 166, *170*
Beauchamp, R. S. A., 58, 59, *68*
Beaufort, L. F. de, 119, *127*
Beeftink, W. G., 124, *127*
Bell-Cross, G., 62, *68*
Biswas, S., 23, *30*
Bleasdale, A., 164, *170*
Bonn, E., 195, *199*
Borutskii, E. V., *153*
Boughey, A. S., 77, *84*
Boulton, A. G., 161, 164, 165, *170*
Brett, J. R., 56, *68*
Brook, A. J., 59, *68*
Brown, A. W. A., 92, *94*
Burney, L. E., 194, *199*
Byrd, I. B., 192, *199*

C

Campbell, R. N., 139, *146*
Capart, A., 65, *68*
Carter, G. S., 34, *41*
Chacko, P. I., 57, *69*
Churchill, B. C., 190, *199*
Collart, A., 65, *68*
Cooper, C., 163, *170*
Crance, J. H., 192, *199*

D

Daget, J., 61, 62, *68*
Dowling, L. T., 174, 178, *181*
Drew, R. L., 130, *135*
Du Plessis, S. S., 57, *68*

Dymond, J., 65, *68*
Dzyuban, N. A., 151, *153*

E

Earle, T. T., 79, *85*
Eipper, A. W., 192, *199*

F

Ferriss, A. L., 190, *199*
Frost, S., 96, *97*
Frost, W. E., 56, *69*

G

Gadd, K. G., 90, *94*, 104, *108*
Ganapati, S. V., 57, *69*
Geen, G. H., 56, *68*
Gilligan, J. P., 190, *199*
Grimalskii, V. D., *153*
Gurin, G., 190, *200*

H

Hammerton, D., 174, 180, *181*
Harding, D., 58, 59, *69*
Harrison, D. S., 81, *84*
Hartog, C. den, 124, *127*
Hasler, A. D., 180, 181, *181*
Hassan, Ahmed, 78, 81, *85*
Hattingh, E. R., 76, *85*
Hayes, F. R., 140, *146*
Heard, W. R., 197, *199*
Heinen, E. T., 78, 81, *85*
Hemphill, J., 191, 196, *199*
Hickling, C. F., 62, 67, *69*
Hickling, G. F., 65, *69*
Hill, K. R., 90, *94*
Hoather, R. C., 165, *170*
Hornby, F. P., 177, *181*
Houghton, G. U., 165, *170*, 174, 177, *182*
Houser, A., 197, *199*
Hughes, J. P., 92, 93, *94*
Hynes, H. B. N., 96, *97*

Subject Index

A

Abberton reservoir, 175, 176
Acacia arabica, on Nile, 44
Acartia tonsa, in Lake Veere, 126
Acroloxus, in Lake Brokopondo, 40
Alabama, small reservoirs, 192, 200
Alestes,
 in Lake Albert, 71
 in Lake Volta, 28
Algae,
 in Lake Brokopondo, 40
 limitation, 180–181
Alternanthera,
 chemical control, 81
 philoxeroides, in U.S.A., 80
Ampullaria, in Suriname River, 34
Angling, in American recreation, 189–190
Anopheles,
 gambiae, and Nile, 44, 45
 multicolor, and Nile, 45
 pharoensis, and Nile, 43–44
 quadrimaculatus, 91–92
Aphanizomenon flos-aquae var. *Klebahnii*, in Brielle Meuse, 121
Aplexa marmorata, in Lake Brokopondo, 40
Arcella, in Suriname River, 35
Archaeological salvage in man-made lakes, 109–111
 from Aswan High Dam, 109
 from Lake Kariba, 109
 from Lake Volta, 109–111
Aswan High Dam,
 archaeological remains, 109
 population resettlement, 99, 100, 101, 105
Aufwuchs, 28, 31, 114

B

Bacteria, in water supply, 174–177
Barrages,
 abolition of tidal changes, 132–133
 biological implications, 129–137
 coarse fish, 133–134

depth of reservoir, 132
 invertebrate fauna, 133
 migratory fish, 134–135, 142–144
 productivity of water, 129–131
 turbidity, 131–132
Belostoma, in Lake Brokopondo, 40
Bilharzia vectors, 41
Braakman, 121
Brielle Meuse, 121
Brokopondo, *see* Lake Brokopondo
Bush, clearing, 18, 22, 61–63, 114
Bythothrephes, 153

C

Cataclysta, in Suriname River, 34
Catfish, in Lake Brokopondo, 39–40
Ceratophyllum, in Lake Volta, 22, 28
Ceratopteris thalictroides, in Lake Brokopondo, 41, 42
Chrysichthys, in Lake Volta, 28
Chydorus, in Lake Brokopondo, 40
Cichlids, 13
Clams, in Suriname River, 34
Clarias,
 in Lake Volta, 28
 mossambicus, in Lake Kariba, 17
Clearing bush, *see* Bush
Congo River, plant invasion, 78
Corophium, in Lake Veere, 126
Crabs, in Suriname River, 34
Crustaceans, in Lake Brokopondo, 40
Ctenopharyngodon idella, fishery stocking, 65
Cyperus rotundus, on Nile, 43
Cyprinus carpio, fishery stocking, 64

D

DDT, effect on *Simulium*, 92, 96, 97
Delta Plan, Netherlands, 121–124
Deoxygenation, 4, 9, 12, 22, 23–24, 28, 29, 31, 35–37, 58–59, 178, 180
Dictyosphaerium, in Suriname River, 35
Diplodon voltzi, in Suriname River, 34
Distichodus, in Lake Kariba, 13, 17
Dorosoma, 208